Ministry of Defence

The Nassau Connection

The Organisation and Management of the British POLARIS Project

Peter Nailor

LONDON
HER MAJESTY'S STATIONERY OFFICE

ISBN 0 11 772526 9

HMSO publications are available from:

HMSO Publications Centre
(Mail and telephone orders only)
PO Box 276, London, SW8 5DT
Telephone orders 01-622 3316
General enquiries 01-211 5656
(queuing system in operation for both numbers)

HMSO Bookshops
49 High Holborn, London, WC1V 6HB   01-211 5656 (Counter service only)
258 Broad Street, Birmingham, B1 2HE   021-643 3740
Southey House, 33 Wine Street, Bristol, BS1 2BQ   (0272) 264306
9–21 Princess Street, Manchester, M60 8AS   061-834 7201
80 Chichester Street, Belfast, BT1 4JY   (0232) 238451
71 Lothian Road, Edinburgh, EH3 9AZ   031-228 4181

HMSO's Accredited Agents
(see Yellow Pages)

and through good booksellers

Preface

This work was undertaken at the invitation of the Ministry of Defence. Many people in the Ministry of Defence, the former Ministry of Aviation and in the United States Department of the Navy gave most generously of their time, as did representatives of major contractors, notably the Vickers Shipbuilding Group and the British Aircraft Corporation, and a number of participants in the joint United States–United Kingdom POLARIS programme who have now retired from the public service and from the industry. Material derived from these interviews has formed an important part of the material, and has been noted in the text, but without attribution to individuals. My thanks are particularly due to Rear Admiral C. W. H. Shepherd, from whom the invitation, and the opportunity to undertake the book, directly arose and to Vice Admiral Sir Hugh Mackenzie, who has given support and encouragement at every stage.

My former colleague, Michael Dillon, has been a substantial contributor to what follows, especially in regard to the material relating to Shipyard Progress and to the interview programme which I have described: but, of course, the responsibility for any errors that may have slipped through remains mine. The bibliography has been amended to reflect additional material that has been published since the monograph was first prepared.

P.N.

For Rufus Mackenzie, and his colleagues on both sides of the Atlantic, who showed that what ought to work in theory can work in practice.

Contents

Glossary of Abbreviations

ACO	The Admiralty Compass Observatory, Slough
AEA	The United Kingdom Atomic Energy Authority
AEC	The United States Atomic Energy Commission
BNBMS	The British Naval Ballistic Missile System (the formal name of the programme commonly called the UK POLARIS Programme)
BUShips	The Bureau of Ships in the US Navy Department
CPE	Chief Polaris Executive (either the Chief Executive himself or his organisation)
DGD and M	The Director General, Dockyards and Maintenance
DGS or DG Ships	The Director General, Ships
DGW	The Director General, Weapons
DOPC	The Defence and Overseas Policy Committee (of the Cabinet)
DPT	DREADNOUGHT Project Team: also Technical Director, Polaris Executive
EB	Electric Boat Company
FBM(S)	The United States Fleet Ballistic Missile (System)
FOSM	The Flag Officer, Submarines
ICBM	Inter-Continental Ballistic Missile
IRBM	Intermediate Range Ballistic Missile
JSTG	Joint Steering Task Group
MLF	Multi-lateral Nuclear Force
MOA	Ministry of Aviation
MPBW	Ministry of Public Building and Works
MRBM	Medium Range Ballistic Missile
OSD	Office of the Secretary of Defence
PLO	Polaris Logistics Officer
R and D	Research and Development
SP	Special Projects Office (in the US Navy Department)
SSHA	Scottish Special Housing Association
STG	Steering Task Group

Introduction

The POLARIS programme was, by any standard of comparison, a significant undertaking. It was urgent, it was costly; it represented, for British security interests as a whole as well as to the Royal Navy, a major challenge to their ingenuity and skill. And it was completed within the required timescale and within the forecast budget. In these regards at least, it has a singularity that calls for some explanation, which is why this book has been written.

It is an account, therefore, of the management organisation and effort that was applied to the programme that was foreshadowed by the agreements reached at the Nassau Conference in December 1962, and reached the first stage of its accomplishment when the Royal Navy assumed the responsibility of deploying the main strategic deterrent force from the Royal Air Force in July 1969. It is incomplete, in the sense that it does not carry the story forward to the equally taxing task of maintaining and servicing the deployed force, nor does it do more than touch on aspects of the operational problems that a submarine-based force has to deal with. The prime concern is to describe and explain how the POLARIS force and its supporting activities were created and set to work.

CHAPTER ONE

The Historical Background

Although the first British atomic device was tested in October 1952, the British strategic nuclear deterrent effectively came into being in the period between 1956 and 1960, when the first generation of V-bombers passed into operational service and, progressively, became equipped with nuclear and thermo-nuclear weapons in the megaton range. In the same period plans were laid for a successor system to replace the V-bombers as the main delivery system.

It was a time of technological change so rapid and so extensive as to be bewildering, when efforts made at the political and military levels to place this awesome new range of force into some sort of coherent relationship with national and alliance interests led, in the West, to confusion and dissension and, in the East, to studied reticence at the military level and occasional bombast at the political level. In the United Kingdom, the initial production programmes, of weapons and of delivery vehicles, were a national and independent activity, but after 1954, and especially after 1957, British success in manufacturing their own weapons opened the way to a resurgence of co-operation and information exchanges with the United States. In the same period, the rapid development of Soviet nuclear capabilities led the United States and the United Kingdom (and then subsequently France) to plan delivery systems which not only utilised the fast developing technologies that reduced the bulk of the nuclear weapons themselves but would look beyond the capabilities of manned flight, on which all the first generation deterrent forces were based. The advent of "hydrogen bombs" changed both the destructive power of a nuclear arsenal and the scale on which such power could be provided: the era of "atomic paucity" which had been based upon the early difficulties experienced in processing enriched uranium was very short-lived, and its passing shifted the crucial cost of a nuclear capability from the weapon itself to the delivery system, which would have both to penetrate defences and be sufficiently responsive to avoid, or survive, a pre-emptive attack.

The first choice for a successor to the V-bombers which the United Kingdom government made, in 1956–7, was BLUE STREAK, a liquid-fuelled missile with a range of about 2,000 statute miles, the design for which was based in part upon the United States ATLAS system. It was

1

first designed to be launched from pads but later from under-ground siloes and would take a minimum of ten to fifteen minutes to prepare for launch. BLUE STREAK was preferred to a supersonic bomber design (the Avro 530) which had been expected to take between ten and twelve years before it could be in squadron service. BLUE STREAK was cancelled in 1960 as a military project. Cost was not the only reason for cancellation; part of the increase in cost was attributable to pioneering research into the problem of "hardening" the siloes and could have been represented as a necessary improvement. BLUE STREAK was overtaken by technology, especially by the development of reliable solid-fuel rocket motors that enabled a much higher and more flexible state of readiness to be maintained, and were already under development by the United States and the Soviet Union. The unexpectedly fast development of reliable inertial guidance equipment was also of significance, not least because it enabled much greater accuracy to be achieved over very long distances.

Before BLUE STREAK was cancelled, however, the United Kingdom government undertook a general review of its policy which, while it naturally concentrated upon hardware options, also sought to establish strategic aims and parameters. The consequences went beyond nuclear weapon systems, to include new arrangements for planning and controlling all research and development programmes, and also extended to an agreement to provide facilities in Holy Loch for United States naval forces and a decision to buy SKYBOLT air-to-surface missiles.(1) If SKYBOLT could be successfully developed and be mated to the V-bombers, it would prolong their active service life; but even though the deal was attractive on these grounds, as well as for its relatively cheap purchase price free of research and development costs, it still represented only a short-to-medium term solution. The general development of new air defence systems was seen as putting a finite limit to the credibility of bombers as nuclear delivery systems. For this reason, the review (and the public debate which accompanied it) also considered the possibility of purchasing the United States Navy POLARIS system. This was to be a solid-fuelled IRBM, launched underwater from nuclear-propelled submarines and was the naval analogue of the land-based MINUTEMAN system; they had both grown out of the review of future weapons policy undertaken by the Killian Committee in 1955 for the US Department of

(1) Strictly speaking, this was not a "package deal" in the sense that the SKYBOLT deal depended upon the Holy Loch agreement. The latter was in line with earlier agreements to allow the forward deployment of US deterrent forces, and the former represented a new level of co-operation in nuclear systems between the US and UK governments. But, from the British point of view at least, the two agreements moved consistently towards the dual aim of strengthening Anglo-American ties and of improving British capabilities.

Defense and were both at the stage of advanced development trials.(2)

The attraction of the POLARIS system for the United Kingdom was that it would enable the nuclear force to be moved out to sea, away from the highly vulnerable homeland, and would provide a more credible second-strike deterrent. These particular advantages of the system for the United Kingdom were noted as early as May 1957 by Senator Henry Jackson (Dem.: Washington), in a speech to the United States Senate.(3) His remarks provided ammunition for Mr. Patrick Wall in a debate on the Navy Estimates in the House of Commons in March of the following year.(4) But the purchase, or the construction, of an adequate POLARIS force looked as if it would cost considerably more than it was expected that SKYBOLT would cost; and it would involve the shift of responsibility for deploying the deterrent from the RAF to the Royal Navy. The RAF was unwilling to envisage this possibility, and the Navy was unenthusiastic.

A. J. Pierre says of this situation:
"In retrospect the failure of the Royal Navy to make a strong case to the Cabinet for acquiring POLARIS rather than SKYBOLT before, and at the time of, the BLUE STREAK cancellation, was an irresponsible mistake. The Admiralty had been watching the development of POLARIS closely since 1956 and recognized that it was an ideal strategic system for Britain because it was not subject to surprise attack (as was any weapon located on British soil), because it permitted a delay in retaliatory action (and, therefore, gave time for verification of the source of an enemy attack and consultation with the United States), and because it moved the nuclear force away from the homeland. But the Navy chiefs were not enthusiastic about POLARIS, being worried about its costs and the accompanying drainage of skilled technicians. The 'senior service' was more interested in maintaining the 'traditional' navy of surface ships which controlled the seas and was fighting for a new generation of aircraft carriers. It was unwilling to sacrifice a 'balanced' fleet on the altar of a seaborne nuclear force. The Board of Admiralty, therefore, put forth strong reservations to the entire 'independent deterrent' concept, rather than advising the Cabinet that if it was the Government's political policy to maintain the nuclear force, POLARIS was

(2) For a general account of the US POLARIS system and the organisation which developed it, the Special Projects Office, see H. M. Sapolsky, *The Polaris System Development*, (Cambridge, Mass. M.I.T. Press, 1972). Chapter 2 deals with the early period of development following the Killian Committee report. Early in 1954 there had been a technical breakthrough in the miniaturisation of warhead components and in February 1955 the Killian Committee strongly recommended the development of an IRBM of some 1500 n.m. in range as well as an ICBM. The general political environment is described in President Eisenhower's memoirs, *Waging the Peace* (New York, Doubleday, 1965), pp. 206 et seq.
(3) The text of Senator Jackson's speech, delivered on 27 May 1957, is reprinted in his book *Fact, Fiction and National Security* (New York, Macfadden-Barkell, 1964) pp. 59–66.
(4) *House of Commons Debates*, Vol. 583, cols. 1056–1057 (4 March 1958). See also *Stability and Survival* (London: Bow Group, February 1961) and *The Sunday Times*, 9 February 1958.

the most suitable weapon system for it. If the cost of the POLARIS submarines were to be separated, so that either they were not part of the regular Navy budget or the budget was proportionately increased, there would have been less opposition to the Navy's taking over the deterrent mission. But given the past rigid pattern of defence allocations this was not considered likely to occur. Nevertheless, some senior Navy officers acknowledged that the choice of SKYBOLT in 1960 was perhaps only a 'postponement' of POLARIS, and that the undersea missile might become the successor to SKYBOLT in the 1970's."(5)

The period between 1957–1961 was dominated by an extensive, and at times bitter, debate about nuclear weapons and their place in the wide range of British defence policy problems. The arguments ranged from a high ethical level, relating to disarmament, or at least arms control, through the field of international politics and the impossibility of full dependence upon American undertakings and nuclear guarantees, to a complex domestic political *mêlée* in which the separate Services were embroiled with the Minister of Defence of the day, and the two major parties conducted their own campaigns, between and among themselves and with the aid of the Campaign for Nuclear Disarmament. The RAF in 1960, saw SKYBOLT as crucial to the maintenance of its principal role, and the Royal Navy was preoccupied with defending itself against a challenge to its importance and utility that was novel and disturbing.(6)

However, they did take stock of what the implications of POLARIS might be. Successive holders of the post of Flag Officer Submarines (FOSM), who were the Board of Admiralty's principal advisers on submarine matters, had good professional relationships with their United States opposite numbers, and were able to report the general state of professional opinion on the implications for undersea warfare of the United States developments, in POLARIS as well as in more general submarine technology; and since October 1958 a staff officer had been added to the British Navy Staff delegation in Washington to liaise with the Special Projects Office. This appointment resulted from a personal approach from the First Sea Lord, Admiral of the Fleet Lord Mountbatten, to the Chief of Naval Operations, Admiral Arleigh Burke. More directly, and as a consequence of the policy review which led to the decision to purchase SKYBOLT, the Board of Admiralty commissioned an investigation which was to identify what the Admiralty would have to do if the United Kingdom decided to procure POLARIS. This investigation was undertaken by Rear Admiral M. Le Fanu, who had recently been the Director-General, Weapons; it was taken formally by the Board in July 1960, and became, in essence, a blueprint on which future action could be

(5) A. J. Pierre, *Nuclear Politics* (Oxford: Oxford University Press, 1972), pp. 220–201.
(6)The definitive account of the Whitehall in-fighting at this period is given in L. W. Martin's article "The Market for Strategic Ideas in Britain", *American Political Science Review*, Vol. LVI(I), 1962.

based. It was concerned principally with headquarters organisation and manning, and dealt only incidentally with force composition or operational considerations. As a follow-up, and in order to provide a similar brief on technical issues, a team of senior technical personnel went to the United States in the winter of 1960–61 to familiarise themselves with the plans and philosophy of the United States POLARIS programme, which at this stage was being rapidly expanded. The team was led by Mr. S. J. Palmer, then an Assistant Director of Naval Construction, and he, together with the other members of the group, subsequently was a member of the directing staff of the Chief Polaris Executive (CPE). Their report established many of the basic parameters used in the POLARIS programme. All of this was prudent staff-work, unrelated perhaps to the preferences of the Naval Staff, but in line with the public pronouncements of the new Minister of Defence, which clearly envisaged POLARIS as a possible, if hypothetical, successor to SKYBOLT.(7)

In the late autumn of 1962 the hypothesis moved quickly nearer to reality, as SKYBOLT's technical difficulties produced financial implications of major significance to the US Defense Department. The difficulties centred around the problems of providing accurate directional information for a ballistic missile, the launch vehicle for which was itself travelling near to the speed of sound; they had always presented a formidable difficulty, and had been known if not fully understood, at ministerial as well as at service level, for some time. Henry Brandon, Andrew Pierre, Richard Neustadt and other commentators have suggested that the intensity of the Anglo-American crisis over SKYBOLT was related rather more to a range of political factors, including the aftermath of the Cuban missile crisis and misperceptions on both sides, than it was to the particular technical dilemma.(8) Certainly, the initial *demarche* at ministerial level, when Mr. McNamara, the Secretary of Defense, discussed the position with the British Ambassador on 8 November 1962, took the form of an exposition based primarily on economic factors; the price was rising, the date was slipping, and the Secretary of Defense felt obliged to ask the Chiefs of Staff to examine the whole project. The Ambassador emphasised the political importance for the United Kingdom of the project, and the Secretary accepted that the United States would be under a continuing obligation to the United Kingdom if it were decided to cancel: he envisaged three possible alternatives, which were that the British would continue with SKYBOLT alone, that the United States would supply a similar but much less advanced system, HOUND DOG, or that

(7) See *House of Commons Debates*, Vol. 635, col. 1507 (28 March 1960) for Mr. Watkinson's statement. See also *House of Lords Debates*, Vol. 223, col. 1278, for a similar statement in the House of Lords Defence debate by Lord Carrington – the Admiralty was urgently considering "what would be involved in building POLARIS submarines ourselves".
(8) A. J. Pierre, op. cit., pp. 224–231; H. Brandon, "SKYBOLT, the full inside story of how a missile nearly split the West", *The Sunday Times*, 8 December 1963; R. E. Neustadt, *Alliance Politics* (New York, Columbia University Press, 1970), c.3; T. C. Sorensen, *Kennedy* (New York, Hodder and Stoughton, 1965), pp. 564–576.

the US would supply a replacement system, such as MINUTEMAN or POLARIS.(9)

The news caused consternation in London. It was not only a very unwelcome development in itself, but it could not have come at a more fraught time. The President and the Prime Minister had already engaged to meet in the Bahamas in mid-December, after Mr. Macmillan's visit to France; there was therefore no more than five weeks to determine what the United Kingdom's reactions and objectives should be. This left very little time to consider whether a continued dependence upon American cooperation was to be preferred or whether, for example, it might be the time to advance seriously the cause of a European-based collaboration in nuclear weapon development which had, rather earlier, been aired. Militarily it was very important to try and achieve a result which would leave the smallest possible gap between the obsolescence of the V-bombers and the in-service date of whatever was now to supersede them. Secondly, it was now beyond question that the Nassau Conference would take place under tension: some questioning of American motives was bound to arise, and to be linked to the lack of formal consultation which had been experienced during the Cuba crisis;(10) critical British opinion also harked back to Mr. McNamara's Ann Arbor speech in June 1962 when he had advocated the centralised control of Western nuclear armaments, with only a slight bob towards British loyalty to the alliance. McNamara met Thorneycroft on 11 December and the US Secretary again set out the reasons for the tentative conclusion to cancel SKYBOLT: in the interim another weapon trial had taken place and had been a complete failure. Again he set out the possible alternatives, except that now the suggestion for a replacement system had altered to British "participation in a seaborne MRBM force under multilateral manning and ownership". It looked as if the proponents of a NATO Multilateral Force, which had recently been resuscitated as a way of placating some of the allies' wish to be more closely associated with nuclear decision-taking, were getting in on the act. Mr. Thorneycroft by now had been briefed on official ideas

(9) Mr McNamara's concern was precipitated by a revised estimate of development costs to bring SKYBOLT to operational status. The original USAF-Douglas development estimate had been $354m., and the new estimate was found to be $493m. Operational availability had originally been forecast for October 1964, but in 1960 this had been revised to Spring 1965; and in December 1962, in a further revision, sometime in 1966 was being talked of. Five flight tests up to the end of November 1962 had all failed, for various reasons. Every major sub-system, it was claimed, had worked satisfactorily in one or more flights, but they had never all worked satisfactorily together. At the end of December 1962, a sixth flight was declared a success by the USAF, but this claim was flatly contradicted by a Pentagon spokesman (See *Aviation Week and Space Technology* for 17 and 29 December 1962 and 7 and 19 January 1963). The fact of the matter was, as both British and American press commentators noted, that SKYBOLT was no longer as important as it had been in the United States programme; the success both of MINUTEMAN and of POLARIS made it expendable.

(10) Although we know now that President Kennedy frequently telephoned the Prime Minister during the crisis, and that the Foreign Secretary took part in some of the discussions, it is not at all clear whether these conversations were formal government-to-government consultations. See H. Macmillan, *At the End of the Day* (London, Macmillan, 1973), Ch. 7.

about what should be negotiated. A group of officials, at Deputy Chief of Staff level, had considered a range of possibilities. One such was a "hybrid" submarine; a boat armed with eight POLARIS missiles and having good hunter/killer capabilities as well. This hybrid would go some way towards meeting one of the Navy's concerns that a crash POLARIS programme would effectively deprive the Fleet of a number of the nuclear attack submarines that were beginning to enter the construction programme: DREADNOUGHT was virtually complete, and VALIANT and WARSPITE were building or on order. A proposal examined in some detail was that the deterrent force should be mounted in seven such hybrids. The alternative which was also examined was to seek to purchase one or two complete US submarines, and to build perhaps three more in the United Kingdom. Both solutions would be dependent upon the availability of a suitable British warhead, since the government neither wished to be dependent upon American warheads, nor were they available to be bought under existing United States law. The conclusions on these suggestions were that the 'gap' between the V-bombers and the new weapons might be between four and five-and-half years, even with a crash hybrid programme; also it was generally felt that the new version of POLARIS, A3, was desirable, that a British warhead could be made available by January 1969, and that the manpower costs to the Navy would be severe.

The hybrid concept slowly disappeared: McNamara and the US Navy advised against it, both on grounds of cost and because it represented major engineering differences. FOSM was mildly in favour: such boats would certainly be possible to operate and the variety of function might sustain morale. After serious discussions began with the US Navy in January 1963, the hybrid sank from sight, principally because the engineering changes necessary made the weapon system non-identical with the US system, because more manpower would be involved, and because the effect of the new programme on the attack submarine programme proved to be less dramatic than had been feared. It was also the case that the hybrid lost much of its attraction in the context of a force assigned to NATO; otherwise the boats might have been used as dual purpose vessels. At least, that was a proposal that had been mooted, but it rather underplayed the absorbing nature of the deterrent function.

At the Nassau Conference itself, little time was spent on SKYBOLT: the American case for cancellation was clear enough to rule out any question of the United Kingdom going it alone. The essential issue was how far the POLARIS material provided to the United Kingdom should be made available without strings and how far it should be contingent upon participation in a multi-national or multilateral nuclear force under NATO direction. Eventually a compromise was found, with both sides representing their views in a *communique* that has many ambiguities.(11) During discussions the British represented the need for

(11) *Statement on Nuclear Defence Systems*, Cmnd. 1915, 21 December 1962 (London: HMSO 1962).

an ultimately independent force, and the President made the point forcibly that there was a major qualitative difference between SKYBOLT and POLARIS. The one had merely extended the life of the V-bombers, the other would prolong the British nuclear capability well into the 1980's.

The outcome of the Conference was, however, that the Admiralty and the Navy had been made responsible for the provision of a deterrent force to replace the V-bombers; the size of the programme and its shape were as yet to be determined. At the administrative level, there was a basic outline of the sort of organisation that would be required; but it was nearly three years old and unrelated to any specific programme. At the technical level there was a fair degree of general knowledge, though it was concentrated in the experience of a handful of senior officers. At the level of doctrine, there was a range of opinion but no unanimity: a certain degree of relief, perhaps, that the Navy had been given this new and important role, but a degree of concern also about the demands which the programme would create. What was quite certain, however, was that the general reputation of the Service was now at stake and involved in the successful creation of the POLARIS force.

CHAPTER TWO

The Creation of the Framework

The Nassau *communique* established, at a very broad political level, that the United States government would sell POLARIS weapon system equipment and spares on a continuing basis and that the United Kingdom government would use the weapon system to outfit, arm and maintain a force of submarines that would be assigned to NATO but would also remain, intrinsically, a national force. The broader aspirations of the *communique*, that a somewhat similar offer would be attractive to the French government and that the whole might be supportive of the British candidacy to the EEC, were not realised. The details, about what precisely might be involved, still had to be determined, and the first task of the United Kingdom government after the Prime Minister had returned from the Bahamas was to settle down to detail.

The results of the conference gave rise to a good deal of political debate domestically, which intensified after General de Gaulle's rejection of POLARIS and of the British application to join the Common Market at his press conference on 14 January 1963. Criticism of the agreement with the Americans was widespread and, so far as particular issues were concerned, extended to a questioning of the utility of maintaining any separate British deterrent force at all as well as to doubts about the utility and the cost of the POLARIS proposals.(1)

In the meantime the various government departments which were going to be concerned with the implementation of the agreement began to order their forces. The Foreign Office, the Treasury, the Ministry of Aviation, the Ministry of Defence and the Admiralty were the principal agencies involved. The Foreign Office began to consider what supplementary agreements would be required to define the specific terms of supply and sale, in consultation with the State Department: Defence,

(1) See the debate on defence in the House of Commons on 30–31 January 1963: *H. of C. Debates*, Vol. 670, especially columns 955–1079 and 1139–1260. Also *H. of C. Debates*, Vol. 673, cols. 31–164, 221–340; 15 March 1963. The efforts made by the Prime Minister and Minister of Defence, immediately after the Nassau meetings, to allay the criticisms voiced by their own supporters illustrated the degree to which opinion remained suspicious of official pronouncements about weapon costs and expenditures in the post-SKYBOLT period; see *The Times* 25 February 1963, p. 6 for a comment by the defence correspondent that "British planners have not so far grasped what the POLARIS submarine missile system really costs".

Aviation and Admiralty proceeded to elucidate what force would be required, what supplies would be necessary and what organization should be set up. As a part of this last issue, the senior staff of the organization had to be selected: already, on Boxing Day, the then Flag Officer Submarines, Rear Admiral H. S. Mackenzie, had been notified by the First Sea Lord that he would be appointed to direct the naval organisation.

An immediate requirement was to bring up to date the information and the ideas which had previously been collected. As far as organizational forms and relationships were concerned, the Le Fanu report of 1960 provided a blueprint and it was taken out to be reviewed and assessed. The basic principle on which it had been drawn up was that, whatever the formal shape of the organization was to be, there would be a need to push through the acquisition and deployment of a POLARIS force with speed and decisiveness. Admiral Le Fanu's report included an initial assumption that the programme would be an eight boat programme, spread over fourteen years using the POLARIS system with British warheads. Hence the tentative costings estimated the charge on current Navy Votes at 7% initially, rising to 20%–25% as the programme achieved its peak expenditure. These estimates did not include manpower costs of an estimated 6,000 officers and men. The core of the report however was the analysis of the alternative possibilities for an organisation to control the programme: on the one hand, a small group of directing staff, brought together to co-ordinate the separate efforts for the various divisions and departments within the Admiralty, or, on the other hand, a composite project group, hived off from their functional parent organisations, and given a distinctive identity and purpose. Admiral Le Fanu's preferred solution was to establish a strong authority in charge of the programme with a direct responsibility to the Board of Admiralty (although it would not be part of the Board). Financial control and weapon system work would be kept in the hands of such a Chief Executive and his staff. Other work would be sub-contracted out to existing Admiralty machinery with specified staff to supervise the "sub-contracted" work.

The analysis was essentially a limited one, concerned primarily with the effects of the imposition of a hypothetical responsibility within the Admiralty. It was drawn up at a time when the American POLARIS project was still at the development stage, and it did not go into any detail about what sort of linkages there would need to be with the USN. Nor did it do more than state that inter-departmental linkages would be required in the United Kingdom. Relationships with the Ministry of Aviation, both at headquarters and with outstations (particularly the Atomic Weapons Research Establishment) would need to be defined carefully; so, as it happened, would the relationship with the new Ministry of Public Buildings and Works, which was to be set up at the beginning of April 1963 and which took out of the control of the Admiralty many of the responsibilities for buildings and maintenance which had previously been the purview of the Navy Works Department. The Le Fanu report had only touched inferentially too upon the extent to which the form of the organisation would need to reflect the types of demand that would be placed upon it, in terms of time-pressures, or budgetary constraints. This was understandable, in the sense that it had been devised for no particular situation; but it also reflected the nature of the model upon which Admiral Le Fanu's analysis had been based. He had very much in mind the type of organisation which the United States Navy had established to manage and control their own POLARIS programme: he had visited Special Projects Office (SP) in order to see how it worked and he had consulted, among other authorities, the CBNS and the staff liaison officer who had been appointed to maintain contacts with SP in October 1958. After the initial possibility of procuring POLARIS had passed away in 1960, the post had been maintained, although the direct utility of the connection had diminished by the summer of 1962 to a point at which it no longer seemed essential to maintain the post. Fortuitously however the post was maintained, to be very helpful in 1963.

There were obviously very considerable differences which had to be taken into account, and Admiral Le Fanu, who had been one of the first of the new Directors General in the Controller's Department, was aware not only of the Anglo–US disparities but also of the relative novelty of the British organisation into which any POLARIS project group would need to be interpolated, or on to which it would have to be grafted. The Controller's departments had been reorganized into Directorates General, somewhat in the style of functional Bureaux, in 1958 following the report of a departmental committee under Sir Barclay Nihill;(2) but the first major new construction programme that had been started since that time had itself been organised as a cross-departmental project, to supervise and monitor the building of the Navy's first nuclear-propelled submarine, the DREADNOUGHT. For a considerably larger project, the choice seemed to be, as the Secretary of the Admiralty put it to the Board in late December, either to create a microcosm of the Admiralty, which could as a separate entity work in parallel to the Department as a whole, or to use the existing departmental machinery.

A third option was that neither extreme alternative should be adopted, and that the Board should set up a project-type organisation, on the general lines recommended in the Le Fanu report, but with some important alterations. The head of the organisation should be a naval officer, of a sufficient seniority to be on a par with the Controller's Directors-General, but with a specific remit and the authority to deal with and report directly to the Board. He should have a naval assistant (who later became CPE's deputy), in a role analogous to that of a chief staff officer: a technical staff, covering ship, weapon (and, subsequently, logistic) issues, and a senior civilian assistant, who would deal with financial, general policy and staffing matters. There would need to be a liaison staff in Washington, and well defined links with the Ministry of Aviation. It had already been agreed – at official, though not yet formally at ministerial,

_____

(2) See *Select Committee on the Estimates, Ninth Report, H. C. 263,* 1961–62. *Her Majesty's Dockyards.*

level – that the Admiralty should have complete responsibility for procuring the missiles and the whole of the missile system from the United States, but this did not solve all the issues that might arise, particularly the degree of direction, or control, that the project director could exercise over Ministry of Aviation staffs.

There was an important issue too relating to responsibility within the Admiralty. The formal responsibilities of a number of heads of department included provision for duties relating to the exercise of professional supervision, maintenance of standards affecting safety or stability and the obligation to enforce these desiderata: the Directors General, Ships and Weapons were the appointments principally concerned but the Chief Inspector of Naval Ordnance and the Director of Armament Supply were also involved. Not only would it be difficult to divide or set aside these responsibilities; it might in practice be impossible to do, because of the shortage of suitably qualified personnel that could service two parallel organisations. So it was proposed that staff appointed to the Polaris Executive, as the new organisation was to be called, should be categorised in one of three ways. The head of the organisation and his immediate staff would be appointed in the ordinary way, with a unitary responsibility; other staff, with a professional obligation to, say, the Director-General, Ships (DGS) would be appointed to work in the Executive but would remain responsible for the professional quality of their work to their 'tribal chief'. They were 'allocated staff'. The third category consisted of staff who need not be allocated full-time to the Polaris Executive but who had a function to perform related to the POLARIS programme: examples might be either the designers of sonar displays in the submarines, or personnel managers whose ordinary business might extend to negotiating the terms of service of industrial civil servants in the new base. These staff were 'designated', as being connected with POLARIS but not employed full-time in the programme: they would continue to be responsible for the efficient execution of their duties to their normal head of department but they would be required to meet the needs of the Polaris Executive as well.

It was a device primarily intended to make appropriate staff available quickly without turning the whole Admiralty structure upside down, and to enable the demands and effects of the programme to be readily identified. It sounded clumsy, and looked ponderous on organisation charts but the notion of a dual responsibility was not unfamiliar, either in the Service Departments or in NATO. In the event, it worked satisfactorily and was helpful in containing some of the feeling of disquiet that there was among the Controller's departments that this novel, challenging and potentially prestigious programme was being removed out of the ordinary run of affairs. Such feelings might have been expected to emerge most readily in the Ship Department, because it became clear that the staff of the Dreadnought Project Team would constitute the core of the Polaris Executive Technical Division; they were the only group with nuclear submarine skills, in design or production, and although the interpolation of the POLARIS weapon system and all the associated equipments would impose a very extensive range of new problems upon their expertise, there could be no question of their essentiality.

Some of them had not only been involved in nuclear design work from the DREADNOUGHT but had been associated with the initial familiarisation with the United States POLARIS programme in 1960–61. The heads of the ship and electrical engineering sections, for example, had been members of the technical mission of that period, and had been kept reasonably up-to-date in the interim with general submarine design material through the regular exchange of information arrangements that operated between D G Ships and BUSHIPS. (This routine flow of information ceased after the Nassau Agreements.) The early technical analysis of what would be involved had established a number of important guidelines, besides giving a good general idea of the interactions between the ship and the rest of the system. In particular, it had been shown that the best arrangements for a building programme would be to have submarines completing at six-monthly intervals; on the assumption that there would be two building yards, a six-monthly cycle looked good for testing and tuning, patterns of labour deployment, for crew training and commissioning, and for providing a convenient build-up to a steady operational deployment. But, in January 1963, there was an urgent requirement to ensure that these types of assumptions were still valid; the existing analysis was based on material nearly three years old, when the United States Fleet Ballistic Missile (FBM) programme did not have the same degree of priority or so wide a range of resources at its disposal. The 1960 norms had been based on POLARIS A2: if the United Kingdom was to go for the newer A3 model, up-to-date information had to be got as soon as possible to establish whether the generational supersession was of fundamental significance to the building phase and whether it might make any significant difference to the arguments relating to the size and type of force, which were still not determined.

At the beginning of January therefore, a mission headed by Sir Solly Zuckerman (the Chief Scientific Adviser in the Ministry of Defence) and Vice Admiral Varyl Begg (the Vice-Chief of the Naval Staff), and including Sir Robert Cockburn (Chief Scientist at the Ministry of Aviation) Mr. J. M. Mackay (Deputy Secretary of the Admiralty) and Rear Admiral Mackenzie went to Washington to be briefed on the current and future state of the POLARIS art, and to acquire as much information as possible on which decisions about the new programme could be based. Information relating to a whole range of issues had to be acquired. The two most significant were how many submarines and how many missiles to submarines to procure. At the time, a force of five or six submarines equipped with sixteen missiles each was emerging as the preferred Naval Staff view, in succession to the earlier suggestions about a larger force of 'hybrid' submarines with fewer missiles. The mission also had to learn what it could about the new mark of missile, the A3. More mundane but equally important areas of knowledge, in terms of eventually securing the success of the procurement exercise, included the extent of the supplies, the logistical support and the other assistance that would have to be acquired from the United States, and the best way of providing it at lowest cost: what would be necessary in the way of modifications to United States equipment to make it compatible with British submarines: and what would be the relative advantages and disadvantages of substituting British equipment or components for those of United States origin, bearing in mind the time constraints likely to be set for the programme. Finally, the mission had to be briefed on what were the communication and navigational requirements, especially in the context of ensuring the independent control and operation of the British fleet.

It could not have been a more difficult time in which to be pressed to take major decisions relating to the third attempt to maintain the deterrent force. The desirability of opting for the latest model of missile could be fairly easily established – if it worked. A3 was still not proved, and if the prime virtue of acquiring POLARIS was that the United Kingdom was buying a system that already worked, there was something to be said for going for the A2. To depend upon A3 was to rely entirely upon the commitment of the Special Projects Office to make it work.

The second area of uncertainty was in nuclear propulsion. HMS DREADNOUGHT was virtually complete: but she was powered by a Westinghouse reactor of American design. The British design of power plant, which was to be used in the VALIANT class, and by implication in the POLARIS submarines, was not yet proved. Experience of installation and nuclear submarine construction was limited to the Vickers Yard at Barrow-in-Furness, and the one case of DREADNOUGHT; and it was virtually certain that Vickers would have to take on additional responsibilities as a lead yard.

CHAPTER THREE

The POLARIS Sales Agreement

One of the most urgent requirements in the early months of 1963 was to determine how and in what way the general agreement reached at Nassau should be made specific. In earlier cases of bilateral agreements about purchases of major equipment – for example those relating to SKY-BOLT or the Westinghouse reactor for DREADNOUGHT – the arrangements, either between governments or contractors, had been made as a consequence of detailed negotiations in which both sides had developed a relatively clear idea of what was at issue. The deal was done as the culmination of a process of elucidation and agreement stretching over weeks, and even perhaps months. In January 1963 the position was different: an agreement in principle had been reached quickly and under tension, without the intervening stages of preparation. Neither side could be precisely sure what might be involved, although both sides were required to produce an agreement that gave form to the settlement that heads of government had laid down.

On the United States side, the Special Projects Office had been only on the fringe of preparations for the Nassau Conference; they had provided information to the Secretary of Defense but had not done so with any appreciation of the likelihood of the eventual outcome.(1) The Pentagon had made sure that President Kennedy was well briefed on the POLARIS option and a good general level of information was available on possible force levels, costs and time-scales – though it had been got together hurriedly after the November consultations between McNamara and Thorneycroft.(2)

The British briefing was of a similar sort, and it was not until after Nassau that the fleshing out of detail began. By the middle of January, the Foreign Office was in conversation with visiting American officials and by the end of the month, the State Department sent across to London the text of a preliminary draft. Even before that, British missions under Sir Solly Zuckerman and Vice Admiral Begg at the policy level and at the technical level under Mr. R. J. Daniel, then the Chief Constructor in charge of the ship design group in the DREADNOUGHT Project Team,

(1) Interview.
(2) Interview.

had been to Washington to reconnoitre. They met officials from the Defense and Navy Departments, and from the Atomic Energy Commission (AEC), as well as from the State Department in early January, and the Begg–Zuckerman report was available by 15 January. It highlighted several important points. Special Projects Office had strongly urged a British system as closely related to the FBM system as possible: nuclear submarines with a battery of 16 missiles; no surface ships, no hybrids. Identicality was one of the keys to a speedy transfer of information and assistance. SP also advocated purchasing the A3 missile; they were emphatic that it would be successful, and warned that the A2 missile production lines were planned to close down within the next two years or so. The mission also learned that the Secretary of Defense was proposing to levy an R & D surcharge on the purchased equipment. A satisfactory agreement was only eventually reached after the British Ambassador had suggested to the President that a percentage levy should apply only in respect of development costs incurred after 1 January 1963: in other words that there should be no explicit contributions to the basic R and D costs of the earlier parts of the FBM programme.(3) The impression was gained early on, then, that the detailed financial terms would be toughly contested.

The "deep technical mission" brought back some useful and specific information, which effectively brought up to date the information available from the 1960–61 exchanges. They identified the scope of the initial problems which the Admiralty in particular would be facing, the plans that it was necessary to ask for to begin submarine design work, and the need to set up a programme for equipment procurement that extended to ship fitted equipment available only through the Electric Boat Division of the General Dynamics Corporation, which was the USN's lead shipyard contractor, at Groton, Connecticut.(4)

In the same timescale, the United States sent officials to London: besides Mr. Paul Nitze at the ministerial level, a group of officials from the Special Projects Office. So, by the time that the State Department draft was received, a series of visits had provided enough information to allow a formal negotiation of detailed terms and arrangements to be set up: on 17 February, the British party left for Washington. It was led by Mr. J. M. Mackay, and comprised besides Admiral Mackenzie, officials from the Admiralty, Ministry of Aviation and Ministry of Defence. In Washington they were assisted by Embassy staff, including legal experts. The terms of reference and negotiating brief were drawn up after inter-departmental consultation and, in general, gave Mackay a good deal of latitude; it was clear, however, that there were likely to be a number of difficulties. The most obvious were the specific financial terms, where McNamara's insistence on some sort of R and D levy gave a hint of the distinctions likely to be drawn between generosity and munificence.

(3) This compromise was suggested to the Ambassador by the RN Liaison Officer in SP. See the comment by Pierre, *op. cit.* p. 242.
(4) Interview.

Secondly, it was clear that the US Government would endeavour to relate this particular transaction to its general policy on equipment sales which was currently being evolved; this might in part be acceptable if it eliminated the need for specific Congressional scrutiny, but the Minister of Defence and the Foreign Office were already sensitive to any attempt to rewrite the Nassau understandings in some more general way which would commit the UK to a multilateral nuclear force or a general NATO-wide initiative.(5) Thirdly, although it would be desirable to specify clearly what the agreement was to cover, not least because of the requirements of existing domestic US legislation and US–UK bilateral agreements on nuclear materials and information, it might be difficult, in the existing state of British knowledge, for the team to be sure how precisely the full needs of the British programme should be covered, given that the understanding at Nassau was to make a continuing agreement that was going to last long beyond the construction phase. Allied to this was the need to provide machinery to make the cooperation that would be necessary effective.

The United Kingdom team was made up, in large part, of officials who would be closely involved with the working of whatever could be agreed, and the United States negotiating team, although it was much larger, as "home teams" usually are, followed the same principle. The chairman was a distinguished Service lawyer, Admiral Mott, but the bulk of the party came from Special Projects Office. The AEC and the Office of the Secretary of Defense (OSD) were also represented. Formal plenary sessions between the two groups began on 22 February and were interspersed by smaller bi-lateral meetings as well as national briefings. The United Kingdom team reported progress by telegram to London and, as the difficult areas of negotiation became evident, by telephone. The United States side had a degree of latitude in proposing features and conducting the discussions which illustrated how heavily Special Projects influenced US Government objectives: only in one area, that relating to finance, was the hand of OSD apparent.(6) The Director of Special Projects, Rear Admiral I. J. Galantin, was very much aware of the obligation to create a workable and successful agreement; it was not only an obligation of honour deriving from the Nassau Agreements, but a desirable aim for Special Projects Office itself, to sustain and amplify its record and its reputation. But on the other hand, the American national programme had to be protected; A3 was not yet proven, and the extensions of the FBM programme authorised in 1961 by President Kennedy from 14 to 29 and then to 41 boats were shortly to lead to an intensive ship-completion and system-proving period when, for nearly two years, one submarine a month would join the fleet. The interpolation into this situation later in the year of the THRESHER disaster, with the possibility of urgent and critical shipbuilding alterations, merely heightened SP's concern to ensure that the United Kingdom programme – whatever it turned out to be

(5) See Pierre, *op. cit.* pp. 243–251.
(6) Interview.

– should not delay or otherwise intrude upon the FBM schedules.(7) Consequently the negotiations, and the shape of the provisional agreement, evolved around the SP input. This was nowhere more clearly shown than in the discussions about the right to manufacture equipment.

The British were concerned to acquire a sufficient level of information to give them an opportunity to manufacture equipment in the United Kingdom. The reasoning behind this was not only to assert a capacity to maintain independence but, more evidently, to save dollars: where equipment was of a more or less standard type, why not have it made in Britain? Admiral Galatin, strongly urged by Admiral Levering Smith, the Technical Director of the FBM programme, opposed this view. There was a political overtone; the United States negotiators had to take account of the possibility of domestic criticism that the deal had been too generous: American jobs might be lost, patent rights transferred and so on. More fundamentally, Admiral Smith argued that the philosophy of a successful deterrent system depended crucially upon a validated assurance that the system would operate successfully if required. This rested, not upon regular and frequent test firings such as might be possible for conventional artillery, but upon the quality and the reliability of the installed equipment, monitored continuously and made identical to the greatest possible degree in each class of ship.(8) If the USN assumed the responsibility to provide a working, and proved, system, the Royal Navy would be able to check the performance of its own ships through the body of reliability data that the US programme was steadily accumulating. This would be a very clear, and great, advantage. On the other hand, to provide the technical and engineering support to ensure the quality and reliability of any modified parts in a small programme of four, or perhaps five, boats would be extremely costly and would reduce the perception of reliability upon which the system, as a deterrent, was based. It was a difficult point to negotiate, because of the sensitivities on both sides and because it involved, for the British, a dependence on the capacity and intentions of SP upon which they were not yet in a position to rely. The definitions about what constituted the essence of the "joint programme" had consequently to be carefully drawn up,(9) but was successfully achieved; the realisation that the additional programme of direct procurement from the Electric Boat Company that would be necessary would cut down the area of interface definition around which this issue revolved was of assistance here, in reaching agreement and in adding impetus to the conclusion of a contract between the Electric Boat Company and the Admiralty.(10) The definitions of what constituted the POLARIS system

(7) Interview.
(8) The practice in the FBM programme in relation to test firings was for each crew to fire practice missiles during final proving trials and after refits, and only rarely at any other time. Only one firing has ever been made of the complete launch-to-explosion sequence of an operational missile.
(9) For example in Article 3 of the *Polaris Sales Agreement, Cmnd. 1995*, April 6 1963; see Appendix I for the text of the Agreement.
(10) Interviews.

so far as the "joint programme" was concerned also had to take care not to include the missile warhead or the nuclear propulsion system but to define the interfaces in a way that would allow British equipments to fit and to function.

It was perhaps inevitable that the size of the task of interpreting the Sales Agreement should be underestimated but quite early on in the negotiations, the two sides agreed that the level of detail that could be foreseen would require some ancillary documentation. They therefore devised the "Technical Arrangements", which were to be procedures and definitions, jointly agreed, relating to specific issues or problem areas and intended to be of use at the working level. This formula proved to be of great significance and eventually became the standard mechanism for defining and then resolving what specific management problems were and how they could be handled. Technical Arrangement sections were negotiated, approved by the Project Officers, and promulgated through-out the joint programme management structure.

By the end of the first week in March, a good deal of detail had been covered in the negotiations, and provisional agreement reached on many points.(11) The main area of difficulty remaining was the financial terms. It had already been accepted by the Prime Minister and the President that a surcharge should be paid, to provide a contribution of 5% towards R & D costs; it was to be limited to equipment coming into service after 1 January 1963, which meant in practice that it would only be paid by the United Kingdom if the A3 missile was chosen. If A2 was chosen, no R & D levy would arise. This surcharge was to be limited to equipment costs, and would not be levied on services. An R & D surcharge was normal practice in equipment sales – and the standard UK charges at the time ranged from 7% to 14%. During the Sales Agreement negotiations, the United States side argued that British orders of equipment should be tied in with American orders wherever it was practicable to do so: not only would some financial benefit be likely to accrue to both sides from larger batch ordering, but there would be less likelihood of clashes of priority that would impede either national programme, and the whole business of inspection and test would be easier. This would however also mean that United Kingdom orders for equipment would have to be determined by timescales that were related primarily to United States needs; in the early months of the programme it meant that CPE was dependent heavily upon SP advice about what was necessary (and it created, as we shall see, considerable problems, not least in learning how to work the administrative system which SP had evolved). It also meant that, on occasion, orders for United Kingdom equipment were placed before they were strictly necessary: and this not only created some difficulties with the Treasury but required extra expenditure for storage. The provision for common contract ordering also threw into sharp focus the need to have a procedure for allocating costs. If the United Kingdom orders had been entirely separate, the identification of costs would have depended upon

(11) For example in Articles II, IV, V, VI, VII, VIII, X, XII, XIII and XV.

the type of contract employed and a fairly standard accounting procedure. The common contract formula required some sort of adjustment, and it was in this aspect of the negotiations that Mr. McNamara laid upon the United States negotiating team specific requirements that resulted in an average cost adjustment formula. Briefly, this provided that costs incurred during the initial building phase (of the British programme) should be allocated according to a formula that would operate over the whole building programme, 1963–69, and that provided for a series of adjustments to be made not only during each successive financial year but at intervals until all attributable costs had been identified. The purpose of this provision was to ensure that the British would pay a price which included some part of the cost of more expensive orders placed at the beginning of a production run; but it was extremely complicated and, the British said, unworkable: more suitable for Chancery lawyers than for financial managers. The Americans privately agreed, publicly explained how they hoped it might work, and both sides relegated to their financial experts the duty to live with it as best they could.(12) The United Kingdom team accepted this position because they still had to take into account the possibility that the British government would decide to go for the A2 missile: this might well involve the resurrection of a special production line, and in that event average cost adjustment might be a very beneficial arrangement.(13) More important, in political terms, was the demand – also stemming from OSD – for lump sum payments as a contribution towards increased United States overheads. It was undeniable that the interpolation of the United Kingdom requirements into the FBM programme would create extra work: at head office, in the factories, the training establishments and test ranges, and in the storehouses. It was also undeniable that it was common practice in all intergovernmental dealings to make some sort of charge for this type of cost. It nevertheless came as something of a surprise for the British negotiators to be told that specific sums – originally totalling $36 million – were to be attributed to these functions; it looked very much as if McNamara wanted to get back by this device the money which he had 'lost' by the settlement on a 5% R and D levy. Prolonged discussion produced a formula by which $17.5m might be attributed to depreciation and overheads, while the rest of the original sum was said to be 'adjusted' in the levy charges. The Americans could not be pushed further. On 6 March therefore, Mackay reported the *impasse* to London, asking for instructions on this and on some other points. On 13 March, the Minister of Defence reported the views of himself and his colleagues to the Prime Minister; he drew attention especially to the concern which the United States government was showing about establishing precedents *vis-à-vis* their Multilateral Nuclear Force (MLF) proposals, which were then at a high point of activity. Mr. Livingstone Merchant and Admiral Lee were even then touring the NATO European capitals, extolling the virtues of the MLF

(12) Interviews.
(13) Interview.

concept. With the agreement of the Prime Minister fresh instructions were sent to Mackay, who resumed negotiations on 15 March.

The negotiation of the POLARIS Sales Agreement provided an important learning process, especially for the staffs of the officials who, under the terms of the Agreement, became the Project Officers. The SP team were brought into contact with the requirement that had been laid upon them by the Nassau understandings, and, from the first, explored its ramifications jointly with their new partners. The British team, though it was much smaller, and varied from time to time, as various members had to return home to cope with all the matters of basic policy which were being hurried forward to define what the United Kingdom programme was to be, shared in this process and could not but be impressed by the zest and the evident good intentions of their American counterparts. The dominating personality in the negotiations was J. M. Mackay.(14) Physically very tall and impressive, ostensibly dour, and absolutely determined to achieve the best possible result, he was at times as much an enigma to his colleagues as to his negotiating adversaries. There was little in the way of collective discussion in the United Kingdom national briefings: Mackay would keep his own counsel about his objectives, say what he wanted done in the way of detail and go on to negotiate in the plenary sessions with a mixture of bluntness and shrewdness which consistently impressed the Americans and occasionally puzzled his colleagues about what had to be done by way of follow-up action. It was a masterly performance and was a major factor in producing a text which went into great detail, and left no ambiguities except in areas where both sides agreed precision was not possible. The length of the negotiating period, considering the force and clarity of the political fiat, reflected the complexity of the task, and the thoroughness of the negotiations on both sides.(15)

The one area in which it might be said that the negotiators were unable to provide adequately for future needs was finance. The Sales Agreement was explicitly recognised as a continuing agreement, but the average cost adjustment formula, and some crucial parts of Article III,(16) heavily emphasised the initial period during which the United Kingdom force would be built and brought into service; there was an implication – but not a very clearly signposted implication – that new arrangements might then need to be made. The financial specialists on both sides realised this,(17) and the Project Officers came to realise it fairly early on; but both sides also recognised – implicitly – that in the circumstances of 1963, it would be difficult to forecast with any accuracy what the needs of 1970 and later years were likely to be; the United Kingdom programme was still not officially defined, and the state of the United States prog-

(14) Mr. Mackay was then a Deputy Secretary in the Admiralty, but subsequently became a Deputy Secretary in the Ministry of Aviation; he was knighted in 1966.
(15) Interview.
(16) For example, the last part of paragraph 1 and paragraph 2(e) (i) and (iii); see Appendix I for the text of the Agreement.
(17) Interviews.

ramme as it might have been developed by 1970 was still a matter of conjecture.

A provisional text of the Sales Agreement, largely agreed but still with some points reserved by the British delegation, was available in the third week of March. The teams dispersed, and on 29 March Mackay submitted a formal report on the Agreement and the negotiations. He reviewed the text and recommended, in general terms, its acceptance. He drew attention to the references which still remained to legislation and earlier agreements. The Americans still wanted to keep a reference to the Foreign Assistance Act of 1961 in the preamble, and although neither the Foreign Office nor the Ministry of Defence liked the insertion, it would probably make no difference to the operation of the Sales Agreement. (Ministers accepted this position, but still wished to omit it, and on the Prime Minister's representation it was removed from the final text, which refers only to the Nassau conference documents). He drew attention to the limitations which it was proposed to accept on the transmission of information to manufacture equipment in the United Kingdom, and urged that it should not be regarded as a sticking point. He also commented upon the provisions of Article XIV (1) about transference of information to third parties. Historically this type of limitation had been a common feature of specific exchanges of information between the two governments in the period since 1948, but (and here Mackay had the Multilateral Nuclear Force proposals in mind) the general climate might be changing and the UK delegation had reserved its position. The situation in the negotiations had been difficult for both parties. The implicit point being made here was that if POLARIS information was to be made generally available to NATO allies under some MLF concept, the British government would not wish to be automatically excluded from any benefits, either in more generous financial terms or even in manufacturing contracts, that might become available: but, given the thrust of United Kingdom objections to the MLF, it did not want to be seen to acknowledge that the MLF concept might be likely to succeed. (Ministers agreed to let the wording stand.) The First Lord circulated Mackay's submission to his colleagues, and the Minister of Defence held a meeting on 3 April, which sent forward a minute to the Prime Minister: Mr. Macmillan queried a number of points, most substantially about the preamble: and after a final flurry, the Sales Agreement was signed in Washington on behalf of the British government by the Ambassador on 6 April; and a subsequent exchange of formal letters explicitly acknowledged the continuing nature of the obligations which it described.

CHAPTER FOUR

The Organisation at Work

The early months

Meanwhile, the organisation to take responsibility for the British programme was being set up, and being pressed, on all sides, at least to identify the major problems which would need to be faced. The Le Fanu 'blueprint' provided a starting point, but it did not help very much in determining the shape of the organisation outside the Admiralty or in selecting the personnel. Admiral Mackenzie was given a skimpy initial briefing on the aims of the programme as conceived by Ministers and the Board: and accompanied Begg, Zuckerman and Mackay on their January fact-finding mission. On his return, and in the interval before departing again on the Sales Agreement negotiating team, he began the process of setting up programme aims by discussion and argument. He was inhibited in this until his appointment could be announced, and the organisation identified to the rest of Whitehall. There were major difficulties about this, relating to the position in the programme of the Ministry of Aviation. The MOA was responsible for aircraft and guided weapon procurement; they had therefore been the responsible government agency for the SKYBOLT programme. Normally the Admiralty would be responsible only for the procurement of ships and ship-installed equipment; in the SEASLUG programme for example the department's responsibilities in the equipment field were limited to the launcher and the guidance radar. There were a number of reasons why this traditional division of responsibilities needed to be altered for POLARIS. The extent to which the ship and the main weapon system were integrated into a single system concept was greatly enhanced, not least because the ship was a submarine embodying many constraints not normally present in a surface vessel; the urgency to complete the programme indicated a project-type organisation; the analogy with the management of the United States programme pre-indicated Admiralty primacy. And the fact that – to a great extent – the programme was based upon existing hardware cut down the extent of the role that the Ministry of Aviation might be expected to play. It would be wrong however to belittle the importance of the Aviation role: statutorily they bought the missiles (using standard reimbursement procedures for transferring the costs to Navy Votes on

23

issue) and they had to ensure that the interface between the missile and the British re-entry system (which had to be designed) was adequately provided for. This was the part of the United States system for which it was already clear the British government could not, by US domestic law, buy very much equipment or information. By the end of December 1962 Admiral Le Fanu had got a working agreement with his opposite number in the Ministry of Aviation that the Admiralty should have effective responsibility for procuring the missiles and the whole of the associated system equipment except the re-entry system and would be the design approval authority. Mr. Julian Amery, as the Minister of Aviation, was inclined to disagree. The SKYBOLT scars were mollified somewhat by a careful courtesy on the part of the First Lord, Lord Carrington, and a full Aviation representation on the battery of ministerial and inter-departmental committees set up to assist the Polaris Executive.(1) The Ministry agreed to appoint a project officer to co-ordinate MOA and AEA activities in support of the programme. The formal creation of an organi-sational framework did not end difficulties between the two departments, or between their representatives in the programme. POLARIS was very much less salient in the Ministry of Aviation's programme than it be-came in the Admiralty, and it was sometimes difficult for the Polaris Project Office there to marshal resources as CPE became able to do. Admiral Dossor's team were also operating in an extremely sensitive area, where neither SP nor CPE held much sway, and where very precise, and sometimes very ponderous, guidelines for the exchange, handling and use of information had to be observed. In a later period, the setting up of a Joint Re-entry System Working Group provided a mechanism of substan-tial importance for handling the exchange of 'restricted data' information and materials which could not be processed under the term of the POLARIS Sales Agreement. The difficulties that did persist however reflected no divergence about objectives, and no lack of willingness or effort to succeed.

Within the Admiralty there were difficulties also. The design of the British submarines and the management of their construction and test-ing clearly called for staffs of high calibre and, probably, substantial size. On the design and ship production side, it could only mean that the bulk of the DREADNOUGHT group should be transferred: but that raised the

(1) Although it was several months before the supporting Committee structure was complete, the principal elements were (a) the Polaris Interdepartmental Policy Steering Committee, chaired by the Secretary of the Admiralty, and comprising representatives from Admiralty, Aviation, Defence and Treasury, (b) the Polaris Committee (later the Polaris Policy Committee), composed of Admiralty officials at sub-Board level, chaired by the Assis-tant Chief of Naval Staff, and required to deal with major issues of policy including any conflict of priorities or "any case where (CPE) finds himself unable to take or ensure measures for the timely completion of the ... programme", and in 1965 (c) the Polaris Operational Planning Steering Committee, which was to supervise the orderly transfer of planning responsibility to the Operational Commander, and included representatives from the Home Fleet and Submarine command. In addition regular meetings were held, in 1963 and 1964, between the First Lord and the Minister of Aviation, to review progress on the programme.

question of absorbing the SSN programme as well. Insofar as only Vickers Shipbuilding at Barrow had experience of nuclear submarine work the entanglement of the two programmes was inevitable; but it represented a serious blow to the Director General, Ships who saw many of the most exciting professional tasks in his department being siphoned away, and was quite naturally concerned that a lot of his best people were being drawn away as well. The situation in respect of the responsibility for the SSN programme was not resolved until June 1963 when CPE was formally given the responsibility for the management of the hunter-killer submarine construction programme. Admiral Le Fanu was in no doubt at all however that Rowland Baker ought to be the Technical Director of the POLARIS work as he had been of the SSN programme, and Sir Alfred Sims generously supported the decision. Mr. Baker had been head of the DREADNOUGHT Project Team (DPT) since its inception and commanded not only the services of a very capable group of professional and technical staff but their loyalty and – more often than not – their affection. He was a figure of considerable stature, not merely professionally, but in personality. Mildly irresponsible in speech, and occasionally tactless, his dynamism and his firm grasp of essentials made him a colourful and occasionally controversial figure: invigorating to work for and, just occasionally, difficult to clear up after. His experience in nuclear ship design and construction made him well aware of the sort of problems that would arise, not only in working under pressure of time, but also in inducing the achievement of new and taxing standards in design and production. He held the view, which the experiences with DREADNOUGHT had reinforced, that there was a much greater and more direct relationship between ship design and ship production than the formal organisation – the distinction, for example, between the Director of Naval Construction and the Director of Naval Ship Production – implied: designers had to "lap over" into the production field because of the necessity to ensure that their intentions were understood, and to prove that their designs worked. This was increasingly important as the dependence of the whole design upon the efficient working of all the crucial but discrete components became more evident, and was a vital element in achieving the best possible "cradle to grave" maintenance. Especially for a deterrent weapon system reliability was the key function.(2)

On the weapons side there was no group comparable to the DPT team that could be hived off from the Directorate-General of Weapons; it had to be assembled by drawing in, to form a new organisation, a substantial proportion of the Navy's missile engineers and ordnance specialists. The officer chosen to head the group was Captain C. W. H. Shepherd, whose involvement in missilry went back to the early days of SEASLUG;(3) he had been a project and trials officer throughout all the development

(2) Interview.
(3) In April 1956, the infant SP had asked for British assistance, derived from their experience with SEASLUG, in evaluating the advantages of employing solid fuel rocket motors.

stages and had therefore a fairly detailed background in solid fuel technology and launch and guidance problems. He had been to the United States on the first major technical mission in 1960 and had also accompanied the Begg-Zuckerman mission in January 1963. He was therefore well equipped; but he was one of a relatively small number of technically trained officers who either had direct knowledge of the POLARIS system or who could guess at the size and complexity of the new task; and he had a relatively hard task to persuade the Director-General, Weapons (DGW) of the need to delegate the responsibility, and to accept the loss of function from the parent organisation. DGW was anyhow in harder case than DGS, who had already partly "lost" the DREADNOUGHT project; DGW could not but be perturbed by the transfer, at headquarters and from the Fleet, of a significant number of officers with missile, principally SEASLUG, backgrounds, and by demands for relatively high numbers of technical and drawing-office staff, who were anyway in short supply. For many months Captain Shepherd had a good deal of difficulty in arranging personnel transfers, in quality no less than in quantity, and was driven to use rather more technical and drawing-office staff from contractors' resources than he might otherwise have wished.(4)

To a certain extent, however, the ship and the weapon areas represented a relatively simple problem, of how to use, albeit in a novel way, structures and resources which already existed within the Admiralty organisation. In the logistics area, a structure had to be created. On one side, the Naval Stores, Armament Supply and Victualling Departments already existed, to be sure, but as separate entities, with very little in the way of co-ordinating (or controlling) mechanism below the level of the Fourth Sea Lord and the Board. The system worked well enough for internal purposes, although the Fourth Sea Lord and the departments themselves were moving towards closer and more formal inter-relationships; not only did they feel that efficiency would be improved by so doing but new developments, like the introduction of large computers, pointed the same way. Insofar as buildings, machinery and maintenance problems were concerned, there was now a formal departmental gap to be surmounted: the Director General of Dockyards and Maintenance covered a range of responsibilities in these areas, but the old Navy Works Department was in the process of transferring to the new Ministry of Public Buildings and Works (MPBW), which was to be set up on 1 April 1963, and it was by no means clear what effect this would have – except that it would require relationships more in the nature of formal negotiations rather than simple departmental direction, even with the familiar personalities and structures that were transferring to the new Ministry, where they would be smaller fish in a much bigger – if more homogenous

(4) Interviews. The provision of draughtsmen and technical staff was a particular bugbear until the middle of 1964. The employment of drawing-office staff from civilian contractors was accepted by the local Whitley machinery because of the general shortage of suitably qualified people. It was a useful and important innovation at the time, but it inevitably led to some loss – or at least the perception by some of Captain Shepherd's staff officers of some loss – of technical authority.

– pond. For all of these reasons, the Fourth Sea Lord strongly urged the appointment of a Polaris Logistics Officer (PLO), who would draw together these strands and provide a focus to ensure that planning for the provision of adequate material support did not lag behind the rest of the programme. An Engineer Captain on the point of retirement was selected to fill the post;(5) this caused some initial resentment among the Supply departments, which had already allocated staff to work with and for CPE, and which naturally had a preoccupation with their own part of the function. As it happened, however, Captain Bomford was not only able to overcome these transitory feelings by his vigour and by the support he was able to marshal for the Supply departments' needs, but was glad to rely upon the cohesion and professional competence of his civilian colleagues in the supply area, which allowed him to concentrate mainly upon the less well-organised and almost totally novel function of designing and building a new base. The concept of the PLO was a major variation from the "Le Fanu blueprint", only partly occasioned by the MPBW reorganisation; it filled a gap in the Admiralty organisation and was seen by the Fourth Sea Lord as a desirable principle in itself, apart from the need which could be attributed to the urgency of the new programme. It was followed quite quickly by a major reorganisation of the Supply departments and in this sense could be said to have precipitated moves which had been under discussion for some time.(6)

The ship, weapon and logistics groups constituted the core of the technical directorate, and were all, logically, situated in Bath where most, if not all, of their parent or associated organisations were already housed in the Admiralty complex, spread over three main sites, that had been set up as long ago as 1938. An obvious question to be dealt with was, therefore, whether Admiral Mackenzie and the other parts of the Executive's staff should not also be in Bath. If they were not, then it was possible that the cohesion of the Polaris Executive as a corporate grouping might take longer and be more difficult to create; but there was as yet no available accommodation where they could all be sited together. This was eventually to be created, by building a new single-storey block of prefabricated offices at Foxhill, on the south side of Bath, into which all of CPE's Bath staff were moved; it facilitated the maintenance of consistent and rigorous security standards as well as a sense of identity but it was not finally occupied until February 1964. Equally, if the staff was to be split between London and Bath, senior officials in particular would have to accept a good deal of travel between the two places; but this was already a fact of life in the Admiralty generally and would not be a feature special to POLARIS. In any event it was less of a burden than the other travel commitments likely to be necessary between Bath and the prospective shipyard and factory sites.

Neither Admiral Mackenzie nor the Controller had any doubt but that CPE himself should be in London. He would need to be in regular contact

(5) Captain Leslie Bomford.
(6) Interviews.

with Board members and Ministers, and to be available for inter-departmental business. Although his direct responsibilities for operational matters were negligible, CPE would have an important job to do in helping to define operational objectives and parameters: and the Naval Staff divisions and the Ministry of Aviation headquarters were all in London too. Admiral Mackenzie saw himself as the focus through which CPE's needs as an organisation were expressed – in this sense he was Bath's London spokesman – and through which also the government's requirements were specified to the Polaris Executive – in this sense he could act as Bath's London guardian against interference; besides which it became clear early on that although quite unusually specific directives about the priority to be accorded to the work had been issued, it was going to be necessary continuously to keep this sense of urgency alive in the minds of busy Ministers and officials, who had many other things to do, and who had very little real understanding of the scope or complexity of the undertaking which had been set in train. Indeed, at less senior levels, there was no awareness at all of what was going on, at least until the publication of the senior appointments and the distribution of office memoranda, in the middle of February 1963.

CPE's own office was, therefore, set up in the London part of the Admiralty, initially in two rooms and a closet: the Admiral and his secretary in one room, the typist in the closet and everybody else in the other room. Cheerful, bustling chaos ensued for a couple of months until more extensive accommodation could be found, and could only be born because for a substantial part of the time a proportion of the staff was at meetings or on visits, with the result that space at one of the four desks became available. The Principal who was to assist the Chief Administrative Officer arrived in time to see Admiral Mackenzie for twenty minutes only before CPE set off with Admiral Begg to Washington: and it was nearly three weeks before the Principal and the Assistant Secretary to whom he was to work managed to contrive an hour together to make their plans. Innovation could hardly have been said to have begun in these circumstances, but it was the starting point for a sense of commitment, and of involvement, that reflected a similar determination in the Bath office. Eventually, it became too a sense of unity, between London and Bath and between CPE and SPO, that was one of the most pervasive impressions left on the minds of the staff who worked in the organisation. POLARIS was new, and working in the Polaris Executive was novel, exciting, urgent and absorbing.

The London office came, after that febrile start, to consist of four sections. The Admiral's office consisted of his personal staff: a Commander of the Supply and Secretariat specialisation, the Project Security Officer and a clerk/typist. The Naval Assistant was a senior Captain, with a staff of Commanders covering functions relating to crew manpower and training, liaison with FOSM and the Naval Staff, and to the development of plans and programmes. An Assistant Secretary acted as Chief Administrative Officer, responsible for the provision and support of civilian staff, and for the financial management of the programme, as well as for advice on general policy.(7) The fourth section was added somewhat later with the appointment of an American liaison team, paralleling the setting up of a British liaison office in Washington, after the coming into force of the POLARIS Sales Agreement. The Chief Administrative Officer's section provided common services for the office, including the staff for programme evaluation and monitoring, and for staffing the regular Joint Steering Task Group meetings and Technical Arrangement drafting. At its peak in 1966, the London office totalled 38 people, the Bath office, including security and typing staff, 430; the MOA project staff totalled 5, and the Washington office 31. These totals included 'allocated' staff in, for example, the Navy Contracts and Navy Accounting divisions, but not those 'designated' staff whose concern with the POLARIS programme was not full-time.

The first major activity to be faced was the delineation of the shape of the programme. As a matter of construction philosophy the Technical Director urged that there should be maximum standardization, both in relation to United States equipment and between the individual British boats. This would be important not only in design terms but also to achieve the best possible standard of maintenance while the vessels were in service. It was suggested at this time, that VALIANT, then under construction at Barrow, should be reconstructed and enlarged, to become the first British SSBN on the analogy of the first American POLARIS submarine, the U.S.S. GEORGE WASHINGTON which had been similarly redesigned. The Technical Director strongly opposed the proposal and it was dropped.(8) It might have got the first submarine to sea a little earlier, but it would have been at the cost of a good deal of shipyard and drawing-office effort and at the risk of providing a heterogeneous squadron. VALIANT was important as a first-of-class hunter-killer submarine, on which future construction was to be based, and she was to be powered by the first nuclear propulsion unit of British design and manufacture. This design had to be proved as soon as possible, not least because it would be embodied in the POLARIS boats, and insofar as weapon system design details for the missile sections of the submarines would take some time to be produced, there was no point in holding up work in hand either at Vickers, at Dounreay or at Rolls-Royce and Associates. At the same time, the question of continuing with WARSPITE, the second boat of the VALIANT class, was first raised. WARSPITE had been ordered but shipyard work was not so far advanced that the ship could not be laid aside, and it was already possible to foresee that there might be problems in relating work on this contract to the POLARIS work at Barrow. (This later became a major problem: see Chapter Seven.) The Naval Staff naturally wished to keep the boat in the construction programme, but the decision, at this early stage, that she should hold her place was largely

(7) Mr. R. N. P. Lewin, who had extensive experience of inter-governmental material and financial agreements. The Naval Assistant became CPE's deputy in 1964, after Admiral MacKenzie had been ill for a period that coincided with a major intra-departmental wrangle over the selection of navigating equipment (for which, see below).
(8) Interview.

because of the labour imbalance that would occur at the building yard if work were stopped on her before labour could productively be transferred to POLARIS construction. It was already clear, from the information gathered in 1960–61 and since Nassau, that a six month production interval for SSBN's in two streams was a logical pattern of work, derived from the demands of testing/maintenance/refit cycles and economic labour loadings, but the number of boats, and the choice of building yards was not yet settled.(9) Preliminary discussions, at the time of the Begg-Zuckerman mission indicated that a force of four, or even better five, submarines would give good value for money in providing a force at sea that would meet the government's need for an adequate deterrent force. In subsequent discussions, a decision was taken to go for four boats in the first instance, and to reserve a decision on whether to go for a fifth boat until later in the year. The importance of the fifth hull was in providing for an overlap which, between self-maintenance and refit periods, would ensure that two submarines were always on patrol; with only four submarines there would be periods (unless irregular patrol cycles were devised) when only one submarine might be on patrol in the best and most advantageous areas. The controlling factor was seen at this time as the life of the reactor core, which determined both the intervals between refuelling refits and the minimum refit periods, thus also constraining the patrol cycle patterns. In the first planning documents that were issued, four boats were identified as 'firm' and the fifth was 'provisional'.

It was clearly essential to begin detailed planning against the background of a general operating concept, which would establish the major areas on which attention should be concentrated; this was the function of the POLARIS Committee whose first meeting was held on 21 February 1963. It was inevitable that American ideas and experience should be taken as a model against which to set British needs: the United States Navy had been operating F B M submarines in their fleet since November 1960 with great success, and it would have been ridiculous not to use this experience and information. The general pattern of operating cycles, the provision of two crews for each boat in order to maintain a high level of operational availability, and the insistence on high maintenance standards all derived from American practice; and they pointed clearly towards the need for a well-planned operating base, with good workshop and store facilities, for missiles as well as for the rest of the weapon and ship equipments. The principal factors determining the location of this base were maximum operational utility (including access to deep water), safety and cost, and the sites considered included Devonport, Rosyth, Faslane, Loch Alsh, Invergordon and Falmouth. An additional consideration, which was only partly related to cost, was the ready availability of land, for building purposes; if land had to be bought, long delays might ensue. The question of where refits should be done also had to be considered; additional facilities would have to be provided, and although it was desirable that, to save manpower and money, these facilities should

(9) Interview.

30

be shared with the concurrent need to develop refit facilities for DREAD-NOUGHT and the VALIANTS, investigations would have to be made to see what had to be done to ensure that SSBN refits did not run beyond their planned time. By the middle of March it became clear that the best site, on all counts, for the operational base was Faslane, in the Gareloch, which was at that time the operational base for the Third Submarine Squadron. Rosyth was selected as the refit yard. The announcement of the decision was delayed until arrangements could be agreed with Metal Industries Limited for the loss of use of their part of the Faslane jetty in their ship-breaking business, but by the end of April, consultations could begin with the local authorities, the Scottish Special Housing Association, and the other interested parties about what the new base would mean to the area. It was the first new naval base in the United Kingdom since Rosyth was developed in 1909, and the first base calling for any major planning effort since the decision to create the Naval Base at Singapore in 1919.

It was also decided, in the same timescale, to build a training establishment, to prepare officers and men for service in the SSBNs and specificially to train both operators and some maintainers on the system hardware. The instructors for this school, and the crews of the first two submarines, would have to go to the United States for their training if they were to be ready in time, but thereafter there would be a steady requirement for training new entrants to the programme and refresher training for existing crews.

The choice of building yards presented some difficulty. Vickers Shipbuilding at Barrow was clearly identified as one that must be included; the yard had, up till that time, a monopoly of all nuclear submarine work as well as a virtual monopoly of conventional submarine work since 1950. The firm was already familiar with some of the main difficulties that were likely to be experienced in reaching improved standards of quality and cleanliness, and between them the firm and the Government had already spent £1½m. in improving the capital facilities of the yard. Vickers also had an almost unique attribute among shipbuilding firms, in a large and well-manned drawing-office. Effectively therefore the firm was obviously the first choice – indeed the only choice – for a "lead yard". In the present context, to be the lead yard would call for a good deal of effort over and beyond building a "first of class" vessel: it would extend to providing guidance drawings and construction and fitting schedules to other yards to supplement those provided by the Admiralty, the bulk ordering of ship-fitted parts, spares and minor equipments (which BUSHIPS and EB said amounted to 30,000 items for each vessel), and training and indoctrination in the required standards of welding, safety, cleanliness and quality control.

It was at least possible to envisage Vickers building all the new submarines, but it was highly unlikely that the expansion of facilities and the labour force that would be necessary to complete four or five vessels to a constricted time schedule could be justified from any longer term viewpoint: even the most optimistic Admiralty plans only envisaged a hunter-killer being laid down every nine months, and that would not justify a three or four stream construction plan beyond POLARIS. It was therefore decided that Vickers should be invited to build two of the four submarines in the initial programme, and to act as the lead yard. The Controller of the Navy met the firm's representatives to discuss the proposition on 4 February, and a formal letter of intent was sent on 18 February. The question then was to find another shipyard. Two had relatively recent experience in building conventional submarines: Cammell Laird, Birkenhead and Scotts at Greenock. The Royal Dockyard at Devonport was also considered. Cammell Laird was the second largest ship-building firm in the country, but Scotts was relatively small, and it was likely that they would have to link forces with other builders in the area.(10) Representatives from Cammells and Scotts visited Barrow on 19 March to be briefed on the general requirements of nuclear submarine building, and after further discussions with the Admiralty, both firms were formally invited to tender for contracts for two SSBNs on 25 March. It was clear that at this stage none of the main contracts could be based on agreed or fixed prices, but it was proposed that for the second yard, as well as for Vickers, prices should be agreed as work progressed; the firms were to conform to specified reporting and progress requirements and were asked to state their expectations on two issues in particular: the fixed fee they expected as profit (in relation to an estimated construction cost), and the amount of capital they were prepared to invest, as part of the cost of the capital facilities that would be required to meet the contract requirements. The Admiralty would provide some equipment and was prepared to assist with a capital grant.

After examination of the tenders, Cammell Laird were chosen and a letter of intent went to the firm on 7 May 1963, for two SSBNs. Vickers had by then already additionally been given the charge to establish adequate formal arrangements with the Electric Boat Company to obtain the information about ship-fitted parts which neither SP nor BUSHIPS could provide.

Information from the Americans became increasingly important: general briefings, about principles, were still useful and indeed necessary for the people who were beginning to join CPE's organisation in sizeable numbers, but the ship designers, the weapons engineers, and the financiers now needed hard facts and details. It was all very well to set a general aim of getting the first boat on patrol in five and a half years, with the others following at six monthly intervals thereafter, but this would only be possible if good intentions could be turned into action: if planning, ordering and control mechanisms were set up urgently to create and maintain an impetus towards success. Organisationally, the existence of the DREADNOUGHT Project Team meant that at least on the submarine side, a design team (eventually 80 strong) was in being, tight-

(10) Cammell Laird's total work-force at the time was just under 2,500, and Scotts about 800.

ly organised and able to get under way very quickly. The outline design of the SSBN, based upon the VALIANT design, was available for approval by the Board in June 1963; but a lot of detailed work remained to be done (for example in redesigning the main valves in the light of information obtained from the USN after the accident to the U.S.S. THRESHER). A good deal of this detail was not handily available: separate contracts for information, and for the identification and procurement of equipment had to be arranged with the Electric Boat Company, in parallel to the links being established between EB and Vickers.

Even in areas specifically covered by the Sales Agreement it became clear that information was not immediately available. A realisation of what the Joint Programme would mean for SP took some time to work out; the goodwill and the obligation existed, but the documents, at any rate in adequate quantities, did not: and even had they done, SP was responsible for ensuring that they were 'sanitized', to omit details, relating to the ship-propulsion interface and the missile-reentry system interface, for which no provision had been made in the Sales Agreement. Packs of documents and books did not begin to be dispatched until some time after the Sales Agreement had been signed, and the delays led to some frustration and impatience. One of the difficulties was to be sure to extract the most important and necessary information first, and the willingness of SP staff to co-operate helped to mitigate tension and to establish good working relationships. Special Projects management staff had been so preoccupied with their own national programme and with completing the Sales Agreement negotiations that they had not given very much attention to the administrative problems that were likely to arise in passing on large quantities of documents and other information, and a number of specific difficulties arose which were resolved only by individual and sometimes unsystematic initiatives. It was not until September or October that a general set of procedures had been established, and a steady flow of material properly organised.(11)

The first hurdle to clear was to specify to the United States Government what the initial programme was to be based upon;(12) and by the middle of March the only remaining major item to be settled was the choice of missile. A preliminary operational concept was prepared by the Naval Staff at the end of January; by the end of February the POLARIS Committee had determined that the submarines would require an operational base, rather than a depot ship, and that specific provision would be needed for refit facilities; that the submarines should be built so as to give them an inherent capability to operate East of Suez if that should subsequently prove to be desirable, and that, so far as the Admiralty was concerned, the missile system to be procured should be the A3. This proved to be a major and contentious issue between the Admiralty and the Ministry of Aviation. At the time of the original SKYBOLT agree-

(11) Interview.
(12) See Appendix I [Article III (I) of the Sales Agreement].

ment in 1960, the earliest mark of the POLARIS family of missiles, the A1, was undergoing final proving trials, and the A2 was beginning flight trials;(13) by the time of Nassau, A2 had been in service as a proved system for over a year. Firing trials of the bigger and more advanced A3 were under way, and the submarines to carry the system were under construction. There was no doubt at all about the soundness or operational validity of A2; and there were British warhead designs already in being which could be adapted to fit.

The safest posture for the United Kingdom government was to delay a choice, to wait until the operational characteristics and reliability of the A3 system were proved one way or the other.(14) But this was the one option they could not choose; if the British submarines were to be built in the shortest possible timespan, the orders for equipment must be placed soon – and if the choice was to be A2, the orders for the fire-control, launcher and navigation subsystems must be placed almost at once, before United States contractors passed on irrevocably to the A3 equipment. In any event the United States authorities were pressing, in the Sales Agreement negotiations, for an early identification of United Kingdom choices so that they could themselves make plans to provide the assistance which was their obligation. In the Ministry of Aviation the engineers and scientists, consulting Sir Solly Zuckerman's staff, grappled with calculations of risk which were all too familiar to them as R and D problems: were the difficulties with A3 transitory or were they fundamental? Ought the government to be advised to be satisfied with a solution of *adequacy*, accepting A2 as good enough for their purposes, and not run the risks which still seemed real enough not only to threaten this third attempt to maintain the nuclear deterrent, but once again to put us upon the rack of dependence on American assertions and an engineering effort in which we had no effective part to play?

The Admiralty was in no doubt what it wanted. Even before a joint Navy-M O A exploratory mission went to Washington in early March to try and establish what the precise position was, it pointed out the undoubted advantages of the A3. The great increase in range was an enormous benefit and increased operational flexibility several times over and the system was designed to give much greater accuracy, at all ranges, and some opportunity for further development. Finally, A2 was to go out of production not later than 1965 – long before the British submarines could be operational: it would then be an obsolescent system, and the British and American main deployments would not be compatible. The general thrust of the argument centred on two points.

(13) A1 1250 nautical miles, A2 1500 nautical miles range: A2 had originally been intended to be the standard equipment but A1 had been adopted, as a technically less demanding concept, in order to meet the accelerated deployment plan ordered in 1958.
(14) The A3 test programme began on 7 August 1962, and 34 test launches were undertaken. The eventual score was: – *Land pad launches;* 23:9 "only partial" successes, 14 successful *Launches from U.S.S. OBSERVATION ISLAND;* 9:4 "partial", 5 successful *Launches from SSBNs*; 2: both successful. See *Aviation Week and Space Technology*, 4 May 1964.

The Admiralty was concerned with the advantages of the A3 system as a whole, while the Ministry of Aviation was preoccupied with the missile; and the Admiralty believed that the commitment of the US Navy, and Special Projects in particular, to make the A3 system work satisfactorily was so great that, in effect, no real risk to the United Kingdom programme would be incurred. The Minister of Aviation still exhibited doubts, and pointed out that a re-entry system design to fit the A3 missile would create many problems. Even after the mission returned towards the end of March, the issue dragged on, and a final confirmatory decision, to go for A3, was not taken until 10 June, and then only after a good deal of pressure from CPE, whose need for detailed information was becoming more and more acute, and whose organisation to process and handle it was now nearly complete.

Provision was made in the Sales Agreement for an exchange of liaison offices in London and Washington, and the head of the British liaison team (SPRN) arrived in Washington on the day the Agreement was signed. Captain P. G. La Niece had, as an Assistant Director in the Weapons Department, been concerned with nuclear safety and had been a member of the Admiralty/Aviation joint mission in March. From this and from his earlier experiences as a staff officer in Washington he already knew a good range of SP personalities, and was generally familiar with the requirements he must fulfil. In general his task was more positive and extensive than that likely to fall to the American liaison team in the United Kingdom (SPUK); SP was the hub of activity, and while SPUK could, and did, perform excellent service in providing information and advice to CPE,(15) SPRN's function was to get to know as quickly as possible how the SP system of management worked, and to use this knowledge to best advantage for the United Kingdom programme: in facilitating the flow of information, in advising on how best to fulfil needs and requirements, and in interpreting British needs to the Americans. The general idea in planning the SPRN team was to have a staff officer, either full time or part time, covering the major areas of the SP organisation. This was particularly necessary in SP's Technical Division, but it was unlikely that enough officers could be made available to provide for this cover on a head-to-function basis, and some other needs were equally important to cover. So, a Constructor was appointed to SPRN's staff but was based at the EB shipyard at Groton, and the Staff Constructor appointed for duty with CBNS doubled up for SPRN's interests in the relevant technical division at the Washington headquarters (SP 26). Other BNS staff, for example in radio and navigational aids matters, also provided assistance. The staff was a mixed naval and civilian office, and a joint Admiralty/Ministry of Aviation organisation, but it was several months before a full complement was finally appointed, and several

(15) The United States liaison team eventually consisted of offices in London and Bath, and specialist advisers in Barrow, Birkenhead and Faslane. Because of the illness of the first senior officer appointed to the London office of CPE, and the difficulty of finding a replacement, the appointment of SPUK was not filled on a normal basis until January 1964.

weeks before the nucleus of the staff had adequate accommodation. In early April, SP had still not really sized up what their new international task was to be: office space was not ready, and the branches, in both the Technical and the Financial Divisions, were not yet fully briefed. Captain La Niece found an early example of this in setting up the Trust Fund. The Sales Agreement made provision for payments in respect of goods and services to be made through a Trust Fund, which acted as a form of contingency account. An initial payment was to be made on the entry into force of the Agreement. Two days after his arrival, La Niece was asked to hold a press briefing and found himself having to deal with questions of detail including enquiries about the Trust Fund payment. What he could not say was that both the British and American staffs had no idea how to handle the payment; Treasury authority to deposit a million dollars had been given, but the Treasury and Supply Delegation in the British Embassy had no machinery for paying in sums of such size in the ordinary way, so they had to draw a cheque on the United Kingdom government account. And the United States government had to discover who might be authorised to receive it! The Finance Section in Special Projects (SP 13) had no authority at that time either to receive monies from foreign governments, or to hold a Trust Fund account that was separate from their own budget; but eventually an office in the Pentagon was discovered that did have an appropriate legal remit and the money was paid over.

Nevertheless SP liaison was very willing and open and, once the Sales Agreement had been concluded, great efforts were made to meet the demands of the Joint Programme.

Unreadiness was also apparent in Whitehall. The difficulties in relation to the Ministry of Aviation have already been mentioned, but there were intrinsic reasons why matters relating to nuclear weapons should be sensitive and difficult to organise. The Treasury too had difficulties; the shift from SKYBOLT to POLARIS, from RAF to Royal Navy, was difficult to evaluate, and the consequences for the rest of the defence programme pointed clearly only to one conclusion: that this new arrangement would produce a bulge in expenditure in the late 1960s. How big it was actually going to be, and how it might be contained preoccupied discussions with the Treasury through the change of government in 1964 until the winter of 1965–66 when the more general questions arising from the Labour Government's first Defence Review shifted the focus and emphasis; the Admiralty held to the view that a notionally separate "POLARIS budget" should be adopted, to identify the costs of the new programme, and to minimize, if not eradicate, the effects upon the rest of the Navy. Insofar as this fitted in with the concept of functional costings, designed to identify and to provide a basis for the better control of particular activities, there was little argument: but the Navy's claim for sanctuary was never conceded in principle. In practice, however, in the early years of the programme, it was not seriously contested, because POLARIS fed on monies that had originally been foreseen for SKYBOLT, and, to a less extent, upon notional savings that arose from the delay of the SSN construction programme. In matters of detail connected with the programme, the Treasury generally co-operated well, although they were prone to delay in issues concerning personnel.(16)

The same was true of the Admiralty itself. The onset of the POLARIS programme was, within the Navy, a controversial matter, centring around the fear that the new responsibility would deleteriously affect the rest of the Navy, the 'proper' Navy. To the extent that this fear could be substantiated, the concern that the Navy would not be given the extra money to provide for the new commitment was based partly upon an awareness of the general pressure under which the defence budget as a whole was placed, and partly from an observation that the V-bomber force had been so well provided for by the RAF that it constituted an *elite* force perhaps even to the extent that other functions and purposes may have suffered. Whether the Navy could now stake a claim for better treatment had yet to be established: but quite early on, the financial specialists in the Admiralty secretariat foresaw that the real difficulties would be likely to arise after the initial building period had been completed and when the question of 'extra' money had to be related to the maintenance, or replenishment, of an existing capability and, of course, when the 'novelty' of POLARIS had worn off. The other and more immediate area for concern was manpower; the manpower bill for POLARIS would be much less than for the V-bombers, but it had to be found from a Navy in which recruiting was already a matter for concern, and where even a relatively generous increase in the allowable numbers in Vote A because of the extra commitment would do nothing at all, either to produce the extra bodies from the free labour market which recruiting had recently become, or to plug the gaps which the diversion of specialist and highly trained officers and ratings to the POLARIS function would, at least in the short term, create. Similar, though less crucial, considerations applied in the civilian field, where shortages, particularly of engineering, technical and drawing office staff, persisted. The initial build-up of CPE's staff illustrated the 'concertina' effect: Admiral Mackenzie himself was relieved at Fort Blockhouse, *pro tem*, by his Chief of Staff, acting as a Commodore and a new Flag Officer was not appointed until seven months later; his Naval Assistant in CPE, and no fewer than three of the initial appointments to Bath and Washington, were hoicked off ships at very short notice. More were to follow, and a number of naval, and civil, appointments elsewhere in the Admiralty had to be left unfilled, some of them for months, while CPE was staffed up. This had to be accepted; but it was not accepted everywhere with the same willingness. It is difficult to generalise accurately, but it is possible to identify a strong current of feeling, particularly among senior officers but by no means limited to the Flag List, that POLARIS was "a frightful chore". Not only was the maintenance of the deterrent a function removed from the traditional range of naval responsibilities, but its inclusion in a submarine force was less than fully welcome. Some submariners at any rate felt that

---

(16) One such example was the delay incurred in settling upon rates of local allowances for ratings under training at the FBM Training Facility, Dam Neck, Virginia.

the Royal Navy was, emotionally, anti-submarine rather than pro-submarine. It was certainly true that in an earlier period, between the wars, the Submarine Service had been at the bottom of the list of priorities for new construction. Submarines and submariners constituted a private navy, separate, secretive and, if the truth be told, rather furtive; it was not very often that they came into regular contact with the rest of the Fleet and even when they did it was to epitomize a threat that a very high proportion of senior officers had spent their careers combatting. It was said that not many submariners reached flag rank, even proportionately to their numbers in the officer corps; and not one, at that time, had ever become First Sea Lord.(17) It was of course true that the submarine service was not the only "private navy"; the Fleet Air Arm had much the same aura, and was much more expensive. But there were structural differences between the two groups which had an important effect. The Fleet Air Arm was much better organised to influence the development of naval policy, even apart from any difference which may have existed because of the great importance of maritime air power in and since the Second World War. FOSM was an operational sub-command, but FO Air (Home) was a major area command, with resources in staff, and support in the Naval Air Divisions of the Naval Staff that the submariners could not, or at any rate did not, match. There was no reserved spokesman for them on the Board, as the Fifth Sea Lord had been for the aviators. FOSM remained the Board's principal adviser on submarine matters, but he was physically removed from day-to-day contact with the rest of the Naval Staff and had little effect upon the day-to-day interplay of affairs. To the extent that there was any substance to these feelings, on the one hand of distinctiveness and on the other of deprivation, then part of the fault lay with the submarine service, and especially with successive FOSM, who did very little to change their position in the system of organisation, and consistently resisted any opportunity to remit any part of their responsibilities to a naval staff division at headquarters.

Methods and management

The lack of knowledge about what the POLARIS programme entailed could not be allowed to persist; it was not only inimical to the position of CPE within the Admiralty, and might give rise to all sorts of misunderstanding and misrepresentation, but might also positively react so as to impede the achievement of the programme's aims, if positive cooperation was withheld. So from every point of view it was in CPE's interest to explain what the programme was and what its effects would – and would

(17) The concept of what a "fair share" of promotions would be is virtually impossible to establish, insofar as only a small number of specialist Captains' appointments were available in the submarine world. Successful submariners, like Admiral Mackenzie himself and Admiral Sir David Luce, who became First Sea Lord, made their careers, and their reputations as senior officers, in other parts of the naval service.

not – be to the rest of the Admiralty and the other Government departments associated in the endeavour. In the early stages, it was difficult to do this except in very general terms, explaining the remit given to the Executive and the authority given to Admiral Mackenzie as the national Project Officer. It became easier from the summer of 1963 onwards, when a series of major decisions had given a finite shape to the programme, when contracts had been initiated and physical signs of progress began to show: and when a sufficient body of United States information became available so that a useful level of detail could be included, in the preparation of illustrated talks and lectures, for naval establishments, reserve units and invited audiences in the CPE Management Centre. Besides exegesis, CPE could practise performance, and this was done principally in two ways. The first was to perform ordinary functions smartly: to issue the minutes of meetings within 48 hours of the meeting taking place, to answer letters promptly, to follow up action efficiently. To be seen to be practising urgency was a virtue in itself: to be known to be the first Admiralty division to procure a Thermofax photocopier, to have authority to make trans-Atlantic telephone calls without question, and delegated authority to approve air passages, all helped in a minor way to establish a reputation for accomplishment – *in posse*, if by no means yet *in esse*. The second way which initially was of Admiral Mackenzie's own choosing but which fitted in very well with the subsequent choice of management techniques, was to emphasise the positive capacity of management: to offer assistance in overcoming difficulties, rather than recrimination. It required the assumption, which it was hoped would be encouraging, that the offender who was falling short of his target was in good conscience striving for the desired end, and merely needed a little help. If the offer was spurned it might be necessary to apply more pressure to ensure that objectives were clearly understood, and to give some explanation to show what the effects of not meeting them might be to the rest of the programme. But the assumption was maintained that the importance of succeeding in the POLARIS programme – for the reputation of the whole of the naval service – was unquestioned and, indeed, unquestionable. If it were not, CPE could raise the matter directly at Ministerial or Board level. But this was an ultimate power, only likely to be useful if used sparingly in ultimate courses; and both CPE and his *confreres* in other parts of the Admiralty were aware of this. But he could, and did, meet regularly with Board members, including the First Lord, and kept them informed of progress, or the lack of it, without necessarily invoking his "right of appeal".

Such practices, however useful in particular circumstances, could not be effective substitutes for a systematic concept of management, though they might help to shape a distinctive style. The organisation of CPE – deriving from the "Le Fanu blueprint" – was a pragmatic, and rather modified, type of project organisation in which a particular set of responsibilities was laid upon an identifiable group. In fact, this was by no means the classical pattern of project organisation; the mixture of responsibilities and resources, and the utilisation of "allocated" and "designated" staff to supplement the core of the project team made it very much an *ad hoc* grouping. In truth it derived from two origins: the defined need to push a special programme through against constraints expressed initially in terms of time-goals, and the perceived desirability of emulating the successful paradigm with which the British programme was to be associated and against which its achievements would stand to be compared: the Special Projects Office. The POLARIS Sales Agreement, with its emphasis upon the connexion between the two national programmes, and the parallel identification of the two national project teams, emphasised the relationship.

A major problem area therefore became the extent to which CPE should adopt – or adapt – SP's management practices; and of course there were obvious and early difficulties. It simply was not possible to conform *in toto*: the legislative and administrative environments were quite distinctively different. The political environments too were quite different, both in terms of overt and general support for the programme and because CPE could never hope to capitalize directly upon SP's proven record of successful innovation. The problems of building a partnership with industry were of a totally different order, as well; and the receptivity of both government bodies and contractors to the requirement to change some of their practices and improve some of their standards had still to be tested. So CPE had to evaluate what SP did – and to establish whether the substance differed from the myth – and then to judge what could be successfully transplanted, bearing in mind that any innovation would have to be of direct utility, and thence of direct appeal. Imitation only for the sake of imitation would cut very little ice, inside or outside the project.

Yet clearly there had to be a measure of compatibility: progress reports, statements of requirements and so on, would need to be in a form that did not complicate SP's own business of getting on with the United States national programme more than was absolutely essential, and would facilitate their understanding of British needs. The British would need to learn how to work the SP system for their own purposes, as well as to use its best features for their own needs; and in order to speed this process, the Admiralty's Organisation and Methods division were asked to make specialist advice available to CPE on a full-time basis, in January 1963.

By this time SP's battery of management techniques had developed very considerably beyond the innovations associated with the early days of the FBM programme, which had become quite well known and widely reported.[18] Several of the most crucial, for example the authority to present and manage a consolidated budget through the Navy Management Fund,[19] had received less public attention than the reporting, estimating and control techniques, like the Programme Evaluation and

---

(18) See, for example, Sapolsky, *The Polaris System Development*, Chapters 2 and 4.
(19) See Sapolsky *op. cit.* pp. 184 *et seq.*

Review Technique (PERT), which had possibilities of adaptation and use outside the government service. One or two, like the system of configuration control, which sought to impose a comprehensive discipline upon engineering documentation and equipment, had received hardly any public notice at all (and consequently could not be "read up"). The general philosophy to which they all related was, in essence, relatively straightforward.

The concept of 'management by exception' provided that programme goals and schedules, drawn up by authorities responsible for their achievement after discussion with SP management, should be coordinated and transmitted by procedures commonly employed throughout the programme so that the whole fitted together; and that these responsible parties should be left to get on with their jobs, seeking assistance from the next responsible layer of management only when they needed assistance. Then, either management support or additional resources would be provided, in a way which ensured as far as possible that the main aim was still achieved. Some functions were less crucial to this main objective than others, so that slippages in time might be tolerable; others might be so essential that virtually any extra cost would be justified, so as not to prejudice the timely and successful completion of the task. To know which was which required an extensive knowledge of the interactions between the various parts of a very wide-ranging and extensive enterprise, and this called for not only special techniques but a monitoring service for senior management which both provided information and a check against overloading the reporting system with too much detail. It also provided a degree of assurance against the honesty of reports, without which the whole concept would become useless. Management by exception called for extensive delegation and trust; from a number of points of view it had been forced upon Admiral Raborn[20] in the early days of SP because he had had little opportunity of creating any highly centralized system of control: the necessary range of resources was not available within the United States government service and the physical spread of the programme throughout the length and breadth of the United States made it unlikely to succeed in any event. His great contribution to the management of the FBM programme had been to turn these disabilities to positive virtues, and he had been greatly assisted by the perceived necessity of the programme in the wake of SPUTNIK, when a successful programme could become equated with a patriotic obligation. The partnership between government and industry was no empty boast. It meant however that many features of the *regime* were totally unfamiliar to the British in 1963, even to those who had some knowledge of more conventional US Navy practices. There was for example a very much greater dependence upon civilian contractors to provide information and assistance, even in matters of equipment design and financial control, than

---

(20) Rear Admiral "Red" Raborn was the first director of SP; he was succeeded by Rear Admiral I. J. Galantin, who in turn was succeeded by Rear Admiral Levering Smith.

Admiralty officials had ever seen: SP had relatively few resources at headquarters and, to British officials' eyes, relatively little knowledge about details.

The seconded O & M staff set up a Programme Evaluation section in CPE's London office in January 1963, and spent a settling-in period assisting the Assistant Polaris Executive develop a simple programme plan which became LONGCAST 1. It was based upon a fixed time-goal which helped to give shape to the emerging pattern of organisation; it was not yet clear what the relationships between the focal points in London, Bath and Washington would become precisely but the general division of function between London and Bath, between general policy and technical affairs, was already evident. It was already evident too that within the sections of the former DREADNOUGHT Project Team, there was already a well-staffed and experienced team used to providing progress information and reports from Vickers Shipbuilding and the DREADNOUGHT and VALIANT. Although it would be desirable for this information to be reported in a style consonant with that which might be used elsewhere in CPE's organisation, there was no good reason – except perhaps to emphasize that the group was now part of a larger whole, whose responsibilities extended beyond linkages with one set of contractors – to upend a working system.

The principal management information techniques to which CPE was attracted could be limited to three: network analysis, programme management plans and stylised management meetings.

The principles of network analysis, or critical path scheduling, had already become known and were already in use in a number of industries, including the building industry. Admiralty experience in the ship field was effectively limited to a pilot study employed during the refit of H.M.S. BULWARK in 1960–61. Initially the attempt was made to apply the technique to the whole submarine construction process with the aim of constructing a 'master network'; the theoretical aim was to create a system of control which spread downwards from the top, but it proved to be extremely difficult to execute and to be fallacious in conception. The reality for this type of technique is to evolve a method of control from the bottom up, and CPE had neither the time nor the resources to allocate to create the linkages that would be required between the relatively small scale networks that were successfully devised. The effective use of network analysis never extended beyond sub-manager level: but it proved useful there, and the effort which was made in 1963 to educate Admiralty and CPE staff in the theoretical use of the technique was eventually justified, insofar that at various levels from Controller of the Navy to main grade professional and senior executive officer, the technique was demonstrated to be useful – but no easy or universal panacea. Eight one day or half day courses were organised, at which an outside consultant demonstrated the utility of the technique; they were simple courses, with the usual risks of over-simplification, but, not least because Board members like Admiral Le Fanu took part and let it be known that their senior, as well as their middle grade, staff should attend also, they did some good in stimulating CPE's image of urgency as well as in general education.(21)

In a similar way, CPE began to develop the use of Programme Management Plans and to embody them in progress meetings. The essential lesson to draw from SP was what management precisely used their control techniques to monitor. The head of the Programme Evaluation Section formed the view, after visiting the Special Projects Office and discussing the issues in Bath and London, with American as well as British colleagues, that there was no point in endeavouring to emulate the independent monitoring function which it was said SP 12 performed for the SP Management Team; it was doubtful from the British point of view whether this function was then sufficiently well developed to be worth emulating and it was pretty certain that CPE could never find the necessary resources for his relatively small programme. What monitoring of managers' reports was to be done would have to be done with CPE front office support, and at least the tacit acceptance of sub-system managers: what CPE could try and transfer direct from SP was the sense of confidence and style.

Programme Management Plans (PMP) are a distinctive form of bar charting, broken down into 'families' systematically from levels of general aims to discrete and particular functions. They identify the agencies who are responsible for or principally affected by *the lack of progress* towards completion: not so that they may be blamed, but in order that they can be warned ahead of time of likely difficulties and assisted in resolving them. A common format allowed standardized reporting at meetings – and discouraged 'representational' reporting. But it meant a lengthy period of initiation and practice, and met with a good deal of initial scepticism. Eventually however the general utility of having a common and relatively simple 'programme language' became accepted, and some of the most vehement early critics became disciples, using the technique in subsequent appointments elsewhere in the naval service.(22) Instructions about compiling Programme Management Plans and other standardized reports were embodied in an Organisation Manual, which was first circulated in January 1964. It also included short job-descriptions for senior and middle management staff throughout the Executive, and the definitions of responsibility *vis-à-vis* CPE and his main collaborators, like the Directors General, Ships and Weapons.

A new and stylized form of fortnightly progress meetings was begun in July 1963, when area, or 'field' managers were required to adopt a common format of report: assessing the current position within their area of responsibility, reporting objectively upon the status of their objectives, identifying forthcoming milestones of significance, and substantiating their analysis of the status if the position was unsatisfactory. It was all a

(21) This small example was quite useful in exposing senior staff to what POLARIS was about. In normal circumstances, knowledge of new techniques, like training courses, tend to be reserved for junior staff: and senior staff hold aloof, perhaps in the mistaken belief that experience is, in every case, a substitute for training.
(22) Interviews. See Appendix IV for details of a PMP 'tree'.

bit theatrical, and frankly emulative of the weekly 'Monday morning meeting' in SP; but it did help to cut across managers' instinctive dislike of owning up to failure, by making it more difficult to hide behind articulate verbiage. The public declaration of the programme's aims helped also to encourage frankness, and the presence of contractors' representatives assisted too. The theatricality, arising in part from meeting in a specially secure conference room and from making one's report from a podium, with standardized graphic aids, was novel and discouraging to the introverted: it was perhaps fortunate that there were very few such in the programme. It also smacked a little of Buchmanite 'fellowship' or the confessionals of the more restrained fundamentalist sects, but on the other hand 'open reports, openly arrived at' did tend to establish a corporate feeling within the programme. The success of such meetings depended upon strong chairmanship which maintained the impetus of the meeting and eliminated mud-slinging. Post-mortems and arguments were reserved for subsequent, private, meetings of the management team. CPE was briefed before the meeting by the Programme Evaluation Section who had the substance of the reports for the meeting at least the night before it took place.(23)

The management team formally consisted of the Chief Executive, the Technical Director, the naval deputy (not least in his capacity as the Chief Planning Officer), the Chief Administrative Officer and the Ministry of Aviation project officer; other directing staff, most notably the deputy technical director for weapons and the logistics officer, attended frequently for specific items of business. The meetings were conducted formally, but there were seldom specific papers to discuss: most of the business arose out of the progress meetings, or from major issues which had previously been discussed informally. The management team operated as a group, after an initial period of assimilation; discussion was not conducted on a 'representative' basis – the progress meetings and the wide dissemination of information which they manifested provided a relatively high level of jointly-shared knowledge which in turn tended to emphasise the corporate nature of the group's function. No member of the team regarded his professional field as immune from discussion, and when a decision was made, it was the result of a joint determination about what should be done.

The development of control and analysis techniques was clearly of considerable importance, especially in a programme in which American and British hardware and management were to be mingled, but it could not displace the need for a management philosophy, which went even closer to the heart of the problem than a general determination to meet time and cost goals. The United Kingdom programme needed to establish what in a normal programme would be called the design philosophy. One of the staff used to explain it thus: "the development of a new system is like first having and then bringing up a baby. An idea is conceived and a system is born: and before it comes into service you have to work out how

(23) Interviews.

it is going to be supplied and serviced. Normally there is time to decide on the limitations and constraints which you think it will be right to impose. The POLARIS programme was like being asked to adopt a baby that already had a personality of its own, and being given a list of its likes and dislikes, and a copy of Dr. Spock: and being told to adapt the rest of the household to this lusty brat's habits while also being required to learn how to change nappies. It is not a very exact simile but it helps to explain in part why the task seemed so absorbing: and why occasionally the baby woke up during the night."

There were a number of considerations which all worked in the same direction. The experience of DPT on the DREADNOUGHT/VALIANT programmes reinforced Rowland Baker's professional instinct that the British POLARIS submarines should, to the greatest extent possible, be standard vessels built identically from a well defined design. This was necessary not only because of the need to house POLARIS weapon system equipment compatibly but because of the need to impose high safety standards and the desire to maintain close control over the shipbuilders' techniques and practices. The weapons engineers, mostly with a background in guided weapons or aerospace, needed no conversion to the ideal of tightly specified standards and procedures, effective throughout the system as a whole. But they had an additional concern, only partly related to the time constraints imposed politically upon the programme; this was to standardize upon United States designs and procedures. It was consonant with SP's advice about design-to-manufacture, and compatible with the responsibility which SP had assumed under the Sales Agreement to ensure the delivery and installation of a working system. It was also consistent with an instinct to reduce any divergences from the successful United States achievement to the absolute minimum; but, in addition, it sought to stifle the equally instinctive urge which every resourceful engineer apparently possesses, to believe that any system or equipment which he has not designed himself is capable of alterations which may be represented as improvements – given time and money. This may be identified as the "N.I.H., or not-invented-here" syndrome; and it is not necessarily xenophobic only in international terms. It sometimes manifests itself in different parts of what is ostensibly the same organisation.

The initial function of the weapon group in the Technical Directorate was therefore to consolidate their information and to test the extent to which it might be possible to enforce the barest minimum of change. At the outset, Captain Shepherd had no set ideas about the form or nature of the technical relationships between SP and CPE, other than a feeling of the need to get as much information as early as possible. He did, on the other hand, have a very firm view, based on his own experience, of the necessity to involve the ship-builders in weapon system testing and tuning, and he shared with Rowland Baker the disinclination to fiddle around with proved designs.(24) The "system concept" was not a novel

(24) Interview.

principle in 1963, but actual experience of the practice in the Service was limited: aerospace and guided weapons were the most obvious examples, where the technical reliability of relatively small components and the need for good safety standards were of a very high priority and evident importance.

How then would the British system differ from the United States F B M package? The ship itself was the biggest area of difference, not merely in relation to the hull but also because supporting equipments like communications and sonar would be of British design and manufacture. Some of these equipments would involve research and development, and although it was in general true that the United Kingdom tended to go for simpler designs than the U S, Captain Shepherd's group was very conscious of the probability that any R & D effort involved the risk of time-lag, of failure to meet the unusually specific time-goals for the deployment of the complete system. Other R & D areas which had to be faced were the re-entry system for the missile, the hovering gear for the submarines, the high quality welding that would be necessary in fabricating the submarine hulls, and a line-of-sight technique that would replace the line-of-sight function of the U S Mark XI periscope.(25) This requirement was the only major consequence of the decision to omit the Mark XI periscope; the periscope had originally been incorporated in the American boats as a multiple function instrument which provided back-up assurance for other equipments in the early days of the United States programme. By 1963 this particular "belt and braces" provision had been obviated by the good performance of the fitted ship's inertial navigation system (SINS). The periscope was not integrated into the weapon system and, with the exception of the line-of-sight function, could be omitted without major effect.

In addition there were a number of areas where British experience, especially in the Royal Navy, was relatively unfamiliar with technical standards embodied in the United States F B M system. No British missile or rocket had employed large diameter solid fuel motors of the size or sophistication of those in the POLARIS missiles, and although it was not initially an area of concern, it became so in 1966–67 when problems of storage, handling and reliability checks had to be mastered. Nor was there much experience with advanced inertial guidance systems, which called for tightly controlled standards of care, and of accuracy. Finally, POLARIS involved specialized on-board and in-flight computing equipment of which the Royal Navy had no experience at all. All of these presented specific problems of familiarization and of learning to cope; problems associated with the production of the equipment were principally and primarily the care of the United States government, on whose agents the United Kingdom had to depend.

(25) Interview.

Problem areas

Discussions with Special Projects about the implications of these areas of policy began in the summer of 1963 as more and more detail began to be added to the outline programme. They focussed on the provision in the initial SP budget for 'management services' where the finance branch (SP 13), in default of any other guidelines, provided for contractors' personnel and services on something of the scale which SP Branches used for themselves. The amount of money thus identified was greater than anyone in CPE had expected, and the British members of the Joint Programme were still sufficiently unfamiliar with SP practices that they had made the implicit assumption that many routine functions, like providing documentation and information, would have been covered by the quarterly overhead contributions. There was also some initial suspicion that United States commercial contractors were trying to enhance their necessity to the United Kingdom programme. Special Projects sent a team to London and Bath in August to explain the basis of the estimates, and of SP's use of contractors' resources, and the matter was raised at the second Joint Steering Task Group meeting in September. The misunderstandings which were revealed caused both sides to articulate their positions with some care and, as a consequence, Captain Shepherd took a group to Washington in October which discussed CPE's thoughts for the delineation of responsibilities for testing and tuning equipment with SP's technical management staff and drew up with them a draft section for the Technical Arrangements which specified these responsibilities in considerable detail. The group, supported by SP and SPRN representatives, then visited the plants of all the major weapon system contractors to explain the agreed policy, and to establish whether, from the contractors' point of view, a workable system had been devised. As a result of this exercise, it became possible within a very short time to identify who would provide what, in terms of handbooks, diagrams, test schedules, test checks, advisory personnel, training programmes, back-up services and so on and, consequently, what the costs would be, and how they would be controlled, in some detail. It proved to be a very important achievement, not only in helping to establish a high degree of confidence between the technical and financial staffs in SP and CPE, but also in establishing a model procedure for dealing with other areas of concern.

One such area was the training school: the Royal Naval Polaris School (RNPS), which was to be built alongside the operating base at Faslane. The original conception for this part of the programme was a fairly generalised requirement for a training facility where initial and refresher training on POLARIS weapon system equipment could be given to submarine crews and some workshop staff. It was accepted that the training of the crews for the first two boats at least, and of the School's instructional staff, would need to be done in the United States, and arrangements were made accordingly; but it was desirable that the School should be set up as soon as possible, and it became increasingly clear that the building of the School offered an opportunity to have a "dry run" in setting an installed weapon system to work. The equipment in the School either replicated or simulated much of the submarine-borne system, except that only one missile tube was incorporated; the functions of the other fifteen were simulated. The United States Navy had two training facilities: one, at Dam Neck, near Norfolk, Virginia, had been in operation for some years and the other, at Pearl Harbour, was under construction in 1963. They were by no means identical in layout and they both had a bias towards maintenance training. This feature made it difficult to use either as a simple model for the RNPS which was primarily aimed at operator training and the difficulty was compounded in two important ways. There was a very sharp difference of view within CPE about how much like a complete ship-type installation the RNPS should be. Captain Shepherd's group became more and more concerned that it should be as close to a ship system as possible, and should, specifically, include Test Instrumentation equipment which would allow the sub-systems to be installed and set to work in virtually the same way as in the submarines. It was a logical extension of this view that Vickers should be made responsible for the installation, testing and tuning. The idea fitted in well enough with the concept that the RNPS should be concerned primarily with operational training, and it had the utility that if the RNPS were built in this way it could later be used as a test-bed, to prove out modifications to components or alterations suggested by Special Projects and even perhaps to test out UK-unique modifications and fire-control computer tapes. The great disadvantage was, however, that this conception would call for a redesign effort which would substantially diminish the chances of being able to use either the Dam Neck or Pearl Harbour layout and installation drawings and diagrams. CPE's London staff and SPRN were chary of allowing this to happen. In the first place it looked as if the Royal Navy might be choosing to perform an important POLARIS function quite differently from the US Navy; from the point of view both of the philosophy of cooperation and of the pressure of time, this might be disfunctional. Secondly, it was by no means clear if the fortuitous advantages about a 'first of class' practice installation would be worth the risk; if the RNPS were for any reason delayed, there would be insufficient time to treat the installation as a 'dry run'. Finally, CPE would be introducing changes and unique requirements into a part of the programme where, it was already clear, SP organisation was unusually complicated from the British point of view: the FBM training facilities were supervised by a subsection of the Plans and Programs Division, and the Technical Division had only a limited degree of knowledge and control in this area. (It also became apparent later that CPE's organisation had to be altered so as to provide specially for an RNPS 'sub-project' group.)

Eventually the CPE Management Team supported Captain Shepherd's proposals, but with some reluctance in the face of the expected difficulties; a specific Technical Arrangement section to cover the work relating to the RNPS was agreed with SP and the personnel in each organisation were supplemented specifically to deal with the separate areas of responsibility. Even so the preparation of documentation, especially for the simulator equipment, was continually a problem area in 1964–5, and it was not until the School building at Faslane was nearly complete, and the weapon system equipment began to be installed in late 1965, that CPE could be sure either that the School would complete on time – the first discrete element in the programme to be commissioned – or that the benefits of the 'dry run' would be able to be applied to the testing and tuning of RESOLUTION and the succeeding boats.

The last great tussle over the definition of the initial programme in 1963–4 related to the choice of the Ships Inertial Navigation System (SINS) equipment for the submarines. In the early days of the United States programme it had been the practice in some parts of the overall weapon system to develop manufacturing capability in two or more contractors' plants. But as the system developed from A1 to A2 to A3, and as the principles of configuration control became more widely applied, the practice lapsed until, in late 1963, the navigation sub-system was the only major area in which there was still, effectively, a choice between suppliers: Sperry and Autonetics. Initially too the sub-system had included three SINS equipments, but in 1963 the US Navy was sufficiently assured of the improved reliability of the equipment to reduce the provision to two SINS in each submarine, and this was a practice which CPE eventually decided to follow. Special Projects had also, in effect, decided to concentrate upon the Autonetics model for its later submarines, although notionally Sperry was still an acceptable alternative supplier.

In the United Kingdom the use of inertial navigation techniques was still in an early stage. The Admiralty Compass Observatory (ACO) at Slough was the R & D establishment responsible for the development of a suitable sub-system for use in the hunterkiller submarines, beginning with DREADNOUGHT. It had evolved a design which intrinsically depended upon a SINS produced by Sperry (UK) that was very similar to the Sperry (US) product. There was, therefore, a case to follow this avenue of development, which would have the advantage of standardizing the navigation equipment in all British nuclear submarines, of whatever type. Against that could be set the disadvantages that the British and American POLARIS boats of otherwise similar configurations would be different, and that the British configuration would be – so CPE felt, – less advanced. Certainly it would be necessary to buy additional SINS and to set up an Ashore Navigation Centre at Slough as a test-bed on which to build up British experience and knowledge. The directing staff at ACO were very keen that this should be done, and they secured the support of the Director General, Weapons and, initially, of the Controller as well.

It was not until CPE had had time to consider what the penalties might be of diverging from the SP configuration that opinion hardened against the Sperry-ACO solution. The initial costs would not be so vastly different, but the design differences, and the difficulties of ensuring compatibility during service, seemed to be of more importance than the Director General, Weapons would allow. Perhaps of most immediate importance was the undesirability of allowing the effective control of an integral part of the weapon system to pass out of the control of the CPE –

SP link which the POLARIS Sales Agreement created; this would not only affect design configuration but, to the extent that the setting up of an ANC would be an experimental development, would introduce additional uncertainties about timescales and the availability of proved equipment as well. This last point was important in respect of the equipment that was needed for the RNPS as well as for the submarines.

The dispute could not be settled within the Polaris Executive; it concerned the development of a general SINS programme for other parts of the Fleet and therefore became a general issue which had to be referred to the Controller, and ultimately to the Admiralty Board. There was a direct antithesis between what CPE believed was necessary and what DGW wanted to do, and although Admiral Le Fanu would have been prepared to take specific US Navy advice, it was understandably difficult for Admiral Galantin and Admiral Smith to intervene directly. They were careful to limit their advice to statements of facts and of SP intentions as they related to the FBM programme; but the disagreement had become so intense within the Admiralty that at one stage, the Controller asked Admiral Bush, the Chief of the British Navy Staff delegation in Washington to check directly with Admiral Galantin that the advice being channelled through SPRN was of SP origin and was not being dominated by CPE's technical staff in Bath. The acrimony was in part a reflection of the smouldering resentment felt among DGW directing staff, over the loss of function which the setting up of the POLARIS technical directorate represented; and although the battle over SINS represented a high water-mark both of importance and of intensity, it was only one of a series of differences between the two organisations that occurred between 1963 and 1965. In February 1964, however, Admiral Mackenzie persuaded DGW to agree to a regular programme of liaison meetings at which differences could be discussed and progress could be reviewed. This device enabled better working relationships to develop, and some differences to be defused; in the same month the Board finally approved that the POLARIS submarine navigation sub-system should be based upon two Autonetics SINS.

The fifth boat

The government decision on the size of the POLARIS force was taken, in January 1963, at a time when neither the financial nor operational implications had been precisely established; for this reason the decision was cast in terms that provided for an option to be taken up on a fifth submarine and for a final decision to be made on the matter before the end of the year. Such a decision would clearly be of some importance. So far as CPE was concerned it would mean the lengthening and extension of the building period, with a good many additional contracts, and details to be determined; it would be logical to place the main building contract with Vickers, but it would also be necessary to order extra equipment from the United States, as well as to extend the overhead payments to SP that became a requirement in the Sales Agreement. So far as the defence budget as a whole was concerned, it would imply additional capital and manpower costs and, in later years, an increased allowance for running costs for the POLARIS force. From the beginning the arguments surrounding the fifth boat hinged upon the balance of advantage between this extra investment in the deterrent force and the opportunity costs that would be created elsewhere; was the cost of the extra hull a sufficiently good investment to offset the effects that it would create – given the assumption that the total size of the defence budget was unlikely to be increased?

The view within CPE increasingly came to fix upon a belief that the fifth boat was necessary to make the squadron a fully cost-effective force. The fifth hull provided a degree of flexibility in operational deployment that significantly altered the Royal Navy's ability to maintain more than one submarine on station at all times; with two submarines on patrol all the time, the deterrent capability would be nearly doubled, with no significant increase in overhead costs over the life of the system. It also gave some flexibility to refit schedules, and might in due time assume considerable importance in allowing improved ship-borne sub-systems to be installed during extended refits. As an addition to the programme, it called for a full outfit of shipfitted sub-systems but it did not call, necessarily, for the purchase of a full load of sixteen additional missiles. With one hull assumed to be in refit, five submarines did not call for much more than sixty four operational missiles, plus missiles under test and re-assembly at the armament depot (although the total purchase of missiles had to allow for test firings and some contingency provision). Moreover, the creation of a second construction line at Cammell Laird meant that a fifth SSBN need not necessarily extend the interruption of the SSN construction programme which had been accepted as one of the general naval consequences of Nassau. It might even be possible too to cut down on the manpower costs of the fifth boat by providing, on an analogy with the missiles, something less than a full complement of ten crews for the five boats. So far as CPE was concerned, the benefits seemed clear; Admiral Mackenzie played a leading part in the discussions about the fifth boat which began in September 1963, and the organisation as a whole came to assume that a five-boat force was not merely desirable but should be the norm.

At ministerial level, and elsewhere in Whitehall at official level, the movement of opinion tended to go the other way, and to assume that the four-boat force was the norm, and the fifth boat an addition. The practical effect of this difference was that in interdepartmental discussions the Navy Department has to assume the onus of making a positive case for the fifth boat, and of trying to obtain a decision at something like the time which had originally been suggested. It was however less important to Ministers to stick to what had been an arbitrary time-scale than it was to CPE, who had to take into account procurement schedules and the subjective effect of any delay upon his United States counterparts. The principal issue which Ministers debated was the difficulty of containing the additional costs in the period between 1967 and 1969 without making adjustments to the conventional weapons programmes of, perhaps, all three services; the immediate extra expenditure involved was about £11m., covering two extra quarterly overhead payments to SP and the long-lead items for the hull, but the eventual extra capital cost would be at least £50m., much of it falling in the 1967–69 period. Extra expenditure, and a larger Defence Budget, would of course only be called for if all the various programmes of development in all three services proceeded according to schedule. Some officials, and some ministers, doubted if this would turn out to be the case; if it did not, the fifth boat costs would not create the 'hump' that the projections indicated; but it was hardly a case that could be advanced at that stage without provoking serious inter-departmental differences. How to contain these costs was not finally determined, but Ministers authorised the announcement of a decision to construct a fifth POLARIS submarine, and official action followed to give effect to the decision.

By the early autumn of 1964, formal agreement had been reached with SP to extend the formal concept of 'the initial building period' by six months, and to pay an extra overhead charge; the shipbuilding contract with Vickers Shipbuilding had been amended, and action was in hand to amend the procurement schedules for equipment to be purchased through SP. Long lead items for the hull and propulsion systems had been ordered. But also by the early autumn it had become clear that the fifth boat was a particularly vulnerable part of the programme which was itself an election issue.(26) Virtually the whole of 1964 constituted an election campaign; an election had, under the Quinquennial Act, to be held before November and, as the months passed by without a dissolution, speeches and pronouncements by leading political figures began to be related more and more openly to the impending election. The Conservative Party leadership frequently referred to the necessity of maintaining Britain's nuclear capability and it was in particular a favourite theme of the Prime Minister. Labour Party speakers, on the other hand, dealt with three main defence themes, although the way in which the issues were raised indicated a wide range of opinion within the party. The most generally adumbrated view was that defence spending as a whole was too great a burden on the economy; the second theme – expressed in a variety of ways – was that Britain's nuclear deterrent capability was of questionable utility, that its standing as an 'independent' deterrent was low and that even as a contribution to the Atlantic Alliance it did as much to create dissension as to enhance cohesion. The third theme was that, specifically on the naval level, expenditure on the POLARIS force inhibited the growth of other capabilities, particularly nuclear hunter-killer submarines. An inference was clearly established that, at the very least, a new Labour government would critically scrutinize the POLARIS

(26) See Pierre, *op. cit.* pp. 251–272, for a very well-informed summary of the period between the Nassau Conference and the General Election of October 1964.

programme, along with other major defence projects; and there was intermittent speculation in the press that it might be cancelled outright.

Against such a background CPE was hard put to it to maintain the momentum which the timescale of the programme required. In particular it became very difficult to get beyond the early planning stage so far as the Faslane Base was concerned. The local agencies in Scotland were, understandably, loth to commit themselves to house-building programmes for which they had no local alternative use, and the Treasury was increasingly concerned about the possible effects of authorizing contracts – principally from the Ministry of Public Buildings and Works – that might not be needed. Nevertheless progress in general was maintained.

While the election was under way, in September–October 1964, a series of briefs was prepared, embodying the most up-to-date material relating to expenditure, estimates, possible cancellation charges and, indeed, almost anything else that a new Government of whatever colouring might want to know. In this respect CPE's position was not much different from the rest of the Ministry of Defence; and shortly after the new Labour government took office, CPE, along with a number of other departmental heads, was called on to make a presentation about the state of his programme to the new Secretary of State for Defence and his departmental colleagues. From then until the end of November, a series of presentations and briefings was made, including one to virtually the whole Cabinet. It emerged fairly early on that while there was a fairly general swell of opinion within the Cabinet to trim the programme in some way, there was no urgent demand to single it out for immediate cancellation; the relatively new commitment to the fifth boat came to be seen as an enabling device which allowed the discussion to be concentrated mainly – though not exclusively – on the size rather than the existence of the programme. Sir William Cook, one of the Chief Scientific Advisers in the Ministry of Defence, prepared a report for the Secretary of State which set out the pros and cons of a force of 3, 4 or 5 submarines, and this formed the basis for most of the debate within the Ministry of Defence. The debate continued through December, and CPE was obliged to point out the difficulties that were arising, and increasing, because of the absence of an authoritative decision; two months had already gone by since the election and the programme was beginning to sag. In early January the Secretary of State formally recommended retaining a four-boat programme, but the Chancellor of the Exchequer plumped for a three-boat force, and the disagreement was taken to Cabinet Committee where the decision was taken to stick with four. A public announcement to this effect was made on 15 February.

The immediate financial effects of the cancellation of the fifth boat were small; some of the ship equipment could be diverted to other purposes, and some of the orders for US equipments and parts could be absorbed in an adjusted spares programme. The nominal saving, to the projected cost of a five-boat programme, as a whole, was between £50m. and £52m., but the actual cancellation charges came to less than a million pounds.

The more general effects of the government's decision are harder to evaluate. From one point of view the determination to retain the programme in any form strengthened CPE's position, perhaps particularly with SP; but within Whitehall the fact that the project had been scrutinized and altered was seen as an indication that political support of the programme was, at the best, equivocal. Even though departmental ministers supported CPE firmly when it was necessary to ask for their help – for example in bringing pressure to bear on contractors – it was clear that CPE was now expected to adopt a low profile: to get on with the job but to keep out of the way and especially out of the headlines.

CHAPTER FIVE

Finance and Budgeting

The management system

The financial management of the British Naval Ballistic Missile System (BNBMS: which was the formal title of the project) had to meet four major requirements. The first was a basic and general obligation to provide financial estimates for forward costings and to assemble accounts of expenditure adequate for both management and auditing purposes according to established government standards. The second was an extension of the first; to arrange for a similar system in respect of expenditure undertaken in the United States on the United Kingdom programme, in order both that dollar expenditure could be monitored and that the transmission of funds, through the Trust Fund which had been set up under the Sales Agreement, could be made in timely manner. The third was to create a reporting system that was sufficiently precise and flexible for CPE's purposes, so that both actual costs and committed expenditure in the United Kingdom and in the United States could be identified readily, and to check that expenditure and physical progress kept in step and matched forecasts given; and the fourth was to provide to CPE generally advice and support on financial planning, contracting and accounting matters.

The general responsibility for the organisation of these functions was the province of CPE's Chief Administrative Officer, an experienced Assistant Secretary with a background in financial management and in dealing with overseas governments. However, with the exception of the arrangements for CPE's office budget, the day to day responsibility for operating the procedures – as well as a great deal of the responsibility for planning them – lay with the 'allocated' staff from the Secretary's Department who had been assigned to the project. A small section of Material Finance Branch I (Mat. I), headed by a Principal, was involved, and brought with it a great deal of experience garnered from the hunter-killer nuclear submarine programme; the head of the section Mr. A. A. Pritchard, was a member of the Sales Agreement negotiating team and was instrumental in setting up both the domestic procedures and the arrangements with SP. A rather larger division of the Navy Contracts Department, under Mr. E. F. Hedger, which had also been primarily involved with nuclear shipbuilding contracts, moved across and became closely involved with both the domestic and the Anglo-American arrangements; and a section of the Navy Accounts Department, under Mr. F. Whitehouse, became almost full-time in support.

The most immediate problem in January 1963 was to ensure that provision was made in the 1963–64 Estimates, which were about to be laid before Parliament. Nominal sums were included in the Ministry of Aviation and Ministry of Public Buildings and Works estimates through the agency of their own finance branches, but the most significant figures were in the Navy Estimates, reflecting not only staff costs, which were the principal elements in the other votes, but provision for the purchase of long-lead items for the submarines and payments to the shipbuilding yards. Cash provision was accordingly made for £6½m. The preparation of a very provisional outline programme budget had been completed by the time of the Navy Estimates debate, but the Civil Lord emphasised in the debate that a full costing had not yet been possible. The cost of equipment and services from the United States government for a force of four submarines was initially estimated by SP to be something of the order of $300m, and the capital cost overall – including the construction of the operating base – was likely to be 'rather more than £300m' in the period 1963–70. These estimates were progressively refined during 1963–64 but until a relatively late stage in the year they depended as much upon the experience and judgment of the team in Mat I about the general level of estimated costs as upon fully costed details of known requirements.

One of the most difficult areas in which to get such details was the cost of the programme of supplies from the United States. There were obvious structural differences between the two governmental systems, even extending to the timing of their financial years. The British ran from 1 April–31 March, the American from 1 July–30 June. Significantly different methods of authorisation not only meant a certain amount of text-book reading on both sides, but gave rise to quite significant problems of assimilation. The British system of annual parliamentary cash grants was, and is, quite a separate exercise from the preparation of a longer term costing which identified programme patterns of planned expenditure; the financial year was a finite phenomenon, with balances of unexpended funds to be struck at the end of each year, and with a rhythmic cycle of review which enabled political as well as administrative changes to be introduced as a matter of course as well as in a moment of crisis. The American system also had political review mechanisms, at the legislative as well as the executive level, but the attribution of funds, through the process of 'commitment' and 'obligation', did not normally require the same type of preparation of estimates and expenditure, and did not lead to anything like the 'log-jam' which was then common at the end of the British financial year. Although the system of auditing was based upon Fiscal Years, the importance of billing, and of striking a balance, in any particular year of account was not as great in the United States as in Britain. Partly as a consequence of distinctions like these, SP had to be asked to provide expenditure forecasts for the Joint Programme which covered a longer period than they were accustomed to prepare for their own purposes, and had to be more detailed. The Trust Fund procedures called for a quarterly estimate of expenditure anticipated in the next periods for 'billing'; in ordinary United States government procedures money was obligated by function and was immediately available for any relevant bills that became due. Early difficulties in estimating arose from uncertainty about specific programme needs, but even when the United Kingdom's needs had been spelt out in some detail, shortfalls in expenditure persisted, and unnecessarily large credit balances built up in the Trust Fund. SP costs forecasts tended to be overestimated, in part because of unfamiliarity with the degree of specificity needed on the part of contractors' billing offices, in part through SP's concern to keep in funds and steer clear of any charge by the General Accounting Office that US domestic funds were being employed on United Kingdom behalf. It was not until 1966, after a number of attempts to revise procedures and when the equipment delivery programme accelerated, that this problem was reduced to proportions that both sides found tolerable.

By the end of April 1963, procedures for identifying and accounting for costs had been agreed; they had to be equally useful to CPE's sections and SP's branches, and allow attribution to functions and to formal accounting subheads.

They represented a complete innovation as far as the Admiralty's standard procedures were concerned and, for Navy Estimates, required a system of reporting that dealt with British equipment and services as well as United States equipment and services that were chargeable to the programme. Other government departments, like the MPBW, made returns to CPE about expenditures under their control so that a complete knowledge of costs, and progress, could be maintained. The activities covered by the programme were broken down into 'line items' – eventually about 280 – each of which was concerned with a discrete activity that was chargeable to one vote and subhead of account; the line item coding expressed these attributes, and identified the 'field officer' in CPE whose responsibility the activity was, in a simple six column digit pattern. Forecasts of anticipated expenditure and reports of incurred expenditure were brought up to date monthly, and every quarter there was a detailed review, in which 'field officers' participated, which revised the costings and evaluated what changes were necessary. The programme budget was also used as a basis for the standard assessments in the annual Estimates cycle and the preparation of Long Term Costings which, by 1963, had become a regular forecasting procedure in the Defence field. The line item coding was, of course, a prerequisite for the mechanised handling and preparation of the detailed material, but it was also of considerable significance in facilitating a widespread sense of financial responsibility at the field officer level; information became readily available, to managers who needed to know what was going on, not what had happened months and months before.

The system, which was discussed with the Treasury and the Exchequer and Audit Department before it was put to the Secretary of the Admiralty for authorisation, worked well from the outset, and after one or two alterations in early 1964, remained the principal working tool for the management of the budget thereafter.

Attempts were made during 1963–64 to link the United Kingdom's purchasing needs with a new Special Projects computer-based programme, the System for Projection and Analysis, acronymically designated SPAN, which in theory would have produced both financial and material progress data.(1) The inputs necessary were however not held to justify the expense that would have been incurred, and a separate form of United Kingdom purchasing programme was devised, initially by the staff in SPRN's office, which would specify what CPE's requirements were; the programme was, in effect, a series of interlocking plans, which identified material needs in relation to timescales and to general planning criteria. Thus, the plan for logistic support began with an introductory exposition of the maintenance and stock philosophy on which the pattern of ordering would be based, and then went on to specify the goods and services in each area, including documentation and delivery, that would be required. The family of documents which together constituted the programme was called 'PEPLAN', and although the last of the major components was not put into final form until 1965/6, the PEPLAN complex represented the culminating stages of the process of learning – on both sides of the Joint Programme – what it was that the British would need to have and what the Americans would have to do to provide it.

The PEPLAN documents were, nevertheless, only general summaries. They had to be supplemented, and indeed could only be activated, by specific purchase orders which had to be sufficiently detailed to provide data on which contracts and instructions to contractors could be based. A draft order would be drawn up, and transmitted by SPRN to the appropriate technical branch in SP, who would check it against the analogous United States needs and practices, perhaps offer suggestions and fill in quantities: it would be costed and then referred back for authorisation or discussion. After authorisation by CPE it would be fed into the SP procurement organisation, and, eventually, turned into a contract. Specific time periods were laid down for the refinement process to turn a 'purchase request' into a 'purchase order': ten days was the norm, although in some instances of major importance, a longer period ensued. Particularly in the early days, when SP was pressing for purchase orders to be placed at times convenient for their own production schedules, CPE depended a good deal on SP's skill, and good faith. It was not an easy process; and it could be argued paradoxically that it was at times made difficult because of the good relations between the parties. CPE's staff was, almost without exception, enormously impressed by the scale of the FBM programme, by the record of achievement and by the evident good intentions of SP management, led by Admiral Galatin and then by Admiral Smith. After the initial and inevitable difficulties in estab-

(1) See Sapolsky, *op. cit.* p. 105.

lishing a pattern of cooperation, United Kingdom confidence in the willingness and in the capacity of Special Projects Office became so marked that a period of over-expectation ensued: the United Kingdom team tended to expect too much, and were perhaps not as rigorous as they might have been in spelling out details, difficulties and assumptions. The SP staff were guilty of this too; they were in effect being asked to explain and to share their methods of doing business, which is very difficult to articulate precisely. Even in those areas where a consciously novel pattern had been created, the procedures had become habitual and sometimes differed from Branch to Branch; where they were routine they represented years of practice rather than precisely presented regulations. As a consequence, it was sometimes difficult to identify and explain key procedures and attributes until a problem arose which required these habitual practices to be specified.

A major example of this 'confusion through goodwill' occurred in the late summer and autumn of 1963 over what SP called 'management services' and what in the Joint Programme came to be known as Contract Technical Services. This was the area of business in which SP relied upon their civilian contractors for detailed knowledge and support, not merely to back up headquarters staff but in some cases to provide what, in the United Kingdom government service, would be thought essential headquarters functions. Thus, for example, the Vitro Corporation provided the staff, the hardware and the software, to produce the documentation essential to the configuration control of the whole FBM system documentation; the Lockheed Missile and Space Corporation acted as the missile system co-ordinators and managers, and the Naval Weapons Annexe at Dahlgren acted, on an agency basis, as the centre for many of the most crucial mathematical investigations of system problems. The crux of the matter was that, in the great majority of cases, the information and data that the British needed to begin detailed work – especially to determine what their needs for procurement and training should be – were available only in contractors' plants and from contractors' personnel. In one area only this had been recognized: in the field of shipbuilding, where separate contractual arrangements had been made with the Electric Boat Company and where the distinction between 'bought-in' and Admiralty-supplied items was sufficiently familiar for CPE staff to be able to make an analogy between United Kingdom and United States practice. In other areas, the extent to which SP had decentralised its activities beyond conventional United States governmental practice was simply not hoisted in: and to SP the practice had become so standard that it was not, in the earliest days, thought necessary to explain the system in any detail. The situation first began to be identified when SP Finance Branch (SP 13) produced a provisional estimate of forecast expenditure in the light of the general statement of the United Kingdom programme, which was discussed in the margin of the first Joint Steering Task Group meeting in Washington in June 1963. The estimates of money to be spent on management services was considerably larger than the British side had expected: they anticipated that requirements on these services would, in effect, be limited to training courses, payment for advisers on site in the United Kingdom, and the preparation of special documentation for CPE's needs. They were surprised to be told that substantial payments would be required to obtain standard and routine information. The initial reaction was that the payment made under the Polaris Sales Agreement for overhead costs ought to cover such matters, and there was some apprehension that major United States contractors were endeavouring to make themselves expensively indispensable. This not only caused concern on financial grounds; from the point of view of technical experience and the building-up of knowhow, it was highly desirable that the Royal Navy should learn as much as possible as early as possible about the intricacies of the whole system – especially since it had been accepted that they should forego the opportunity to manufacture parts in the United Kingdom. The two Project Officers agreed that the problem area should be examined in detail: the United States side to explain precisely what went on, the United Kingdom side to determine what it wanted to settle for in the light of the explanation.

The issue took several months to resolve, but acted as an important learning process on the budgetary as well as on the technical side of the United Kingdom programme. The procurement function in the SPRN office was initially covered only by a Senior Contracts Officer: a finance officer was added some months later. His initial function was to help set up a consolidated budget and shopping list, to fit United Kingdom needs, as they became clear, into SP contracts and also to learn and disseminate information about SP procedures, particularly those relating to authorisation and funding techniques. He was in the early days very heavily dependent upon the good offices and assistance of SP 13. It was difficult to comprehend easily the scope of the organisation and programme that CPE had joined up with. It turned out to be the case that, in the budgetary and contractual areas, there were few standardized procedures; practices differed between SP branches and even between different parts of the same branch. Moreover the practices of SP were being subjected to changes common to the whole of the Defense network, that were the result of Secretary McNamara's reorganisation of structures and procedures involving an extensive centralisation, and standardisation of procurement policies. Insofar as these were all directed towards greater uniformity and more evident control by the Secretary of Defense, Special Projects was one of the 'over-mighty subjects' whose effective independence of action was being scrutinized and curtailed.(2) The general effect of these changes was to lengthen the period of time between the articulation of a requirement and its validation by a formal contract with a company or firm. The requirement had to be reviewed, made as specific as possible and costed as carefully as possible before the contract was negotiated. There was by this time very little competitive or alternative source tendering in the FBM programme; only in the navigation sub-system

---

(2) See Sapolsky, *op. cit.*, Chapter 7, for a description in some detail of the effects which these changes had on Special Projects Office.

was there still an effective possibility of opting between two suppliers and it was in this area that a major problem arose.(3) Nevertheless procurement procedures were, by comparison with British techniques, lengthy and even ponderous.(4) There was virtually no equivalent of the simple 'letter of intent': United States government contracts were very formal documents and their negotiation reflected the relative importance of legal counsel. The function of negotiating was split between the Counsel's office, which dealt with the general terms and conditions of the contract, and the negotiating office, comprising negotiators who were principally concerned with the financial and pricing aspects. In the Admiralty, as in most other United Kingdom government offices, the Contracts Department staff were used to constructing and dealing with all the elements in a negotiation, whereas in SP even relatively minor matters were codified and institutionalized in the Armed Services Procurement Regulations (ASPR). But in 1963 and 1964 these regulations were being extensively revised to allow for the development of new and varied types of contracts including incentives to better contractual performance. In this respect, as in so many others, the United Kingdom and United States governments were making broadly similar responses to broadly similar problems of administration which they had both experienced during the 1950s, principally as a result of the rearmament programme of that period. The difficulties of estimating, and then controlling, the progress and costs of major development programmes had been highlighted by a series of cancellations or of cost overruns, and had been followed by a number of organisational changes and administrative innovations. In the United Kingdom this had been an element in stimulating the reorganisation of the Defence departments into a single entity,(5) and the analysis of the problem of controlling technologically advanced programmes in the Gibbs–Zuckerman Report was to be followed by a major reshaping of the control machinery.(6) The acceptance of a project-type organisation for the United Kingdom POLARIS programme was itself a manifestation of the same concern. In the Admiralty, as in other departments, there was a general movement towards improving the performance and sensitivity of government's contractual relationships with firms as well as in improving internal procedures (and the Ferranti and Bristol Siddeley affairs showed how necessary changes were).(7) Incentive and penalty clauses were being discussed on both sides of the Atlantic and, for the British, contact with United States thinking helped to speed up the pace of innovation. The issues involved were by no means simple. Although incen-

(3) See Chapter Four.
(4) Interview.
(5) The reorganisation took effect in April 1964; after that time the Admiralty became the Navy Department. CPE's London office moved from the Old Admiralty Building to the Main Building, on Horse Guards Avenue, to a suite of rooms snuggling behind the navel of a symbolic but unpleasing concrete deity which decorated the lintel.
(6) The most detailed description is given in the *Second Report of the Select Committee on Science and Technology, 1968–69 (Defence Research, H.C.213*, 27 March 1969).
(7) See the Lang Reports, *Cmnd. 2428 and 2581* respectively on the Ferranti and Hawker-Siddeley contracts.

tive contracts required the identification of target costs, they did not make it any easier to find out what such costs should be in R and D areas where one of the main purposes of the activity might be the exploration of uncertainty. The administrative costs inherent in new styles of contracts had to be related to effect and scale; incentives were difficult to apply in some cases, especially again in R and D work. The Ministry of Aviation had genuine difficulties here in their part of the POLARIS programme; and this perhaps was the basic reason why their procedures were neither identical nor, in one or two cases, compatible, with Admiralty practice.(8)

The business of building up detail in the United Kingdom programme budget was followed up so that by the time of the 1964–5 estimates season it was altogether a more full and reliable forecast, from the United Kingdom and from the Joint Programme standpoint. The expenditure and programme totals came to a capital cost of £345m spread over the years 1963–71, with running costs of about £95m during the same period: thus £20m was included in this total for material and services required by the Ministry of Aviation, and not covered under the provisions of the Sales Agreement.

	Total	1963/4	1964/5	1965/6	1966/7	1967/8	1968/9	1969/70	1970/1
	£m.								
Capital Cost	345	7	39	65	69	70	64	30	1
Running Cost	95	1	3	4	5	12	20	25	25
Dollar Element	$m.								
	440	8	42	69	74	82	84	55	26
	203	4	25	34	38	39	30	18	15

The functional breakdown of the capital expenditure was estimated to be as follows:–

	£m
4 SSBNs	141
Miscellaneous shipbuilding	9
Support costs	47
Missiles and torpedoes	85
R and D	52
US overhead charges	6
UK headquarters costs	5
	£345m

(Note: 'Miscellaneous shipbuilding' included capital grants to the ship-yards, the construction of a new floating dock and the conversion of a Royal Fleet Auxiliary vessel to transport missiles. 'Research and Development' included ship-fitted communication equipments.)

(8) Interviews.

This total neither included provision in respect of a fifth boat in the programme nor purchase of contingency reserve equipment (£6½m) which had been decided upon as a precautionary measure.(9)

Running costs reflected the build-up of expenditure first on training, hydrographic surveys and other preparatory services and then the operational costs of the submarines themselves as they prepared for and then entered service. The continuing element of dollar expenditure was caused principally by proving trials (including the firing of test missiles) and the supply of spare parts for missile system equipments.

The addition of a fifth submarine to the programme early in 1964 called for a revision of the totals, and also for an increased payment to the United States in respect of overheads, to cover the longer building period; it was agreed by the Project Officers that two extra quarterly payments should, in due course, be made. Additional equipments and missiles would also need to be ordered. But, by the time that the fifth boat was dropped from the programme, less than a year later, no major orders relating to the ship had been made: the definition of the initial building period reverted to its previous scope, and cancellation charges on those contracts which had already been placed amounted to less than a million pounds, since some of the equipment which had been ordered as 'long lead' items was able to be used for a later fleet patrol submarine (as hunter-killer submarines had now been renamed). By January 1965, something approaching £180m of the estimated capital expenditure had been either committed or would have attracted cancellation penalties if the whole programme had been abandoned.

'Downstream definition'

During 1965 a number of factors combined to focus the attention both of CPE and SP upon the arrangements for cooperation that would be needed once the initial building phase of the United Kingdom programme had been completed. The most obvious of these factors was the decision of the new British government to continue with a four-boat programme; but almost as salient a matter within the two separate national organisations was the need to prepare financial estimates covering the post-construction period.

In Whitehall generally, the movement towards ten-year budgetary forecasts was now being extended and becoming a standard requirement; within the Ministry of Defence it was already an annual exercise, in which 'the long term costing' was based upon both approved and (towards the end of the costing period) projected plans. CPE was now both in a position to lay long-term plans and also under an obligation to specify what would be required to maintain the completed POLARIS squadron in service.

(9) The contingency reserve consisted of a virtually complete set of weapon system equipments, other than launch tubes, and was intended to be a back-up in the event of an installation mishap.

In particular it became more and more desirable to identify what the 'steady state' need for stores and spare parts would be, and what the material and manpower needs of a long refit would amount to. The first issue raised some major engineering points; would the United Kingdom system remain identical – or as near identical as possible – to the deployed United States system: or would CPE want to be able to select, and perhaps discard, future SP alterations and improvements? And, if that were to be the case, what machinery would have to be set up to make such judgments and, when they were made, to maintain an adequate – and compatible – system of configuration control? The refit problem raised even wider matters: SP themselves had relatively little experience of overhauls involving the deployed A3 system and could give, for the meantime at least, relatively little in the way of precise guidance. CPE's experience about the problems of ship sub-systems and equipment under refit would have to wait, like experience in re-fuelling the nuclear propulsion plant, upon the first refit of DREADNOUGHT. Target times and expenditures could be set but, for the time being they would have to depend upon the realism of the planning being undertaken in collaboration with the Director-General of Dockyards and Maintenance and the staff of Rosyth Dockyard. In the matter of refits, CPE and SP were more nearly parallel so far as the state-of-the-art was concerned than in any other area of the joint programme.

In Washington, SP had a somewhat similar duty to provide long term budgetary forecasts; but although in form this was a standard function, from 1965 onwards it raised problems which impinged directly on the future of the United Kingdom programme. Following the successful development and deployment of the POLARIS A3 system, SP already had approval to develop a more advanced weapon system (which sequentially was identified as B3, C3 and finally, in its eventual form, POSEIDON). Although in 1965 the parameters of the system characteristics had not been finally agreed, it was already envisaged that this development would be fitted into submarines of the earlier POLARIS classes as they became available for extended overhaul. CPE was kept informed of the progress that was being made on the new system in a number of formal presentations at successive JSTGs. One of the major consequences for the joint programme established by the Sales Agreement would be that, at some not very distant date, the A3 production lines would be closed down; and both the United States and the United Kingdom authorities might have to decide upon their gross needs for A3 equipment on a 'once for all' basis. The Department of Defense laid a requirement on SP, in the spring of 1965, to devise a plan for 'efficient missile procurement' for the A3 system; and SP in turn had to consider, in conjunction with CPE, what this would mean for them both.(10)

It was at this stage that a disparity of viewpoints began to emerge about the meaning of the POLARIS Sales Agreement as a continuing

(10) Interviews.

64

obligation. The staff of CPE made the assumption that the whole range of provisions in the Agreement were standard, and intended to be continuous; this would mean that not only the levels of technical assistance but also the existing levels of financial charge would be maintained. SP staff on the other hand argued that although the general provisions of the Sales Agreement had been undertaken, and acknowledged, as a continuing obligation, the financial provisions in particular – and perhaps some of the technical support too – had only been agreed as relevant to the initial building phase of the joint programme. The need would arise as a matter of course therefore not merely to reassess the technical basis of the relationship but also to review the financial terms. There was therefore a common concern at one and the same time to make sensible and responsible arrangements for a period of cooperation that neither organisation could yet discern in detail, and to manage the shift of position without losing the control that was essential to the maintenance of the status and authority which each organisation had within its own national environment.

It was first of all necessary to establish what the size of the problem was, and CPE initiated discussions in June 1965 to discover the range and extent of SP's ideas about future technical relationships as well as the procedures for arriving at longer-term budgetary forecasts. It was possible relatively quickly to arrive at a satisfactory, if temporary, arrangement on budget figures: tentative estimates were available for refit costs, at least so far as the direct POLARIS weapon system costs were concerned, and a number of major issues (like, for example, the practice to be followed on Operational Test missile firings) still had to be decided upon by the United Kingdom, so tentative expenditure forecasts were acceptable in these areas too. The United States side was less inclined to begin serious discussions straight away on technical matters; they agreed that there were likely to be problems of redefinition – indeed it was they who first put out warning noises – but they did not yet feel ready to debate them. The exact shape and timing for the POSEIDON development was not yet firm, and might substantially influence the issues, and some alterations to the A3 system configuration had to be evaluated first.(11) So each side settled down to evaluate their own positions and intentions, and came together first for formal discussions to determine 'areas of the Polaris Sales Agreement which may be limited in time or scope' during the tenth meeting of the JSTG in September 1965, in Washington.

Over the next eighteen months discussions proceeded regularly but slowly, as both sides gave priority to determining what their own national objectives in the joint discussions should be. The discussions within CPE identified four general areas of hardware support that would be

---

(11) The Project Definition Phase for POSEIDON had begun in January 1965, and at the same time SP formally notified CPE of the United States's intention to acquire a lofting capability in the A3 system; *JSTG 9* and *JSTG 8*, respectively.

required on a continuing basis. The first was the routine replenishment of stocks and spare parts: this might become a heavy item of expenditure as major components like missile rocket motors came to the end of their defined life. The second was the replacement of items used in practice firings; the third was the modification packages which might either arise from routine developments under the configuration control system, or might be introduced to prolong system effectiveness. The fourth area was in the nature of a contingency provision, and arose from the need to buy and support new equipment or to replace prime equipments that had become damaged. There were parallel 'software' requirements, for continuing the supply of documentation and configuration control material: for any contract technical services that might be needed: for continued participation in the AUTODIN communication links that supported the stores and spare parts provisioning system, and for assistance from POMFLANT (the Naval Weapons Annexe at Charleston, S. Carolina, where submarines stored up before practice firings). There might also, in the future, be research and development needs, for which United States support would be required – though this was much more conjectural in 1966–67. By the summer of 1967 it had been agreed to undertake a joint review of those sections of the Technical Arrangements which related to a continuing technical function, in addition to determining what the overhead rate of charge should be for United States government services and at government assisted facilities. The agreement to proceed hid a good deal of careful preparation and activity; each Project Officer obtained – on neither side without difficulty – acceptance of the principle that the discussions should take place within the ambit of the Sales Agreement and between the Project Officers; and on the United States side, S P had had to convince the United States Air Force that the undertakings in the Sales Agreement and in the existing Technical Arrangements explicitly meant that the charges for United Kingdom usage of the Air Force Eastern Test Range were to be raised on the same basis as for the United States Navy; i.e. that the Sales Agreement was a Government to Government agreement.(12)

The specific negotiations followed a predictable enough pattern; the United Kingdom side sought to establish and emphasise the essential continuity between the construction phase and the post-construction period, but they also wanted to provide for new situations that might arise. What future supply requirements might be could be worked out over a period of time; but could they include the purchase of 'common stock' equipment that was surplus to United States needs, at beneficial prices? And could such a provision be established in a way that would not overload a United States support system that would increasingly relegate A3 material to a relatively small proportion of its concerns? The United States side, on the other hand, were concerned both to retain the substance of the main obligations which the Sales Agreement represented, and

(12) Interview.

over which there was no disagreement, and also to moderate, on the basis of the experience accumulated since January 1963, the system of co-operation which was limited to an equipment configuration which no longer represented SP's prime concern. One matter was relatively easy to agree; neither side was anxious to retain the average cost adjustment formula which had been introduced to arrive at prices for United Kingdom equipment purchases during the initial construction period. It had proved in practice to be a difficult and long-drawn out series of refining approximations, which displayed no advantages over less subtle accounting procedures, except that, theoretically, the cost of items to the United Kingdom was averaged out over contracts which had not benefited from large batch orderings; in this way the Department of Defense had hoped to get a return that reflected rather more fairly the heavy 'learning curve' costs of the initial procurements for the United States Navy. But it remained the impression within CPE that what was gained on such a swing was lost in the costs of the complicated accounting roundabout that was the consequence. It was agreed that for missiles, equipment or spares delivered after January 1970, the common contract price to the United Kingdom should be either the actual cost, where that was identifiable, or the proportionate share of the total costs for a particular batch or lot.

The major issue remained whether a percentage surcharge should be levied as a contribution towards overheads and facilities in the post-building phases. Both sides were content to leave the surcharge of 5% as a contribution towards R and D costs at its current level (set out in Article XI, 1(b) of the Sales Agreement), but both sides were equally well aware that the effective levels of payment made on this account, as well as on overheads, would vary quite considerably as decisions were made about the level of equipments and services to be procured; thus, if the 1970–80 bill came to, say $300m overall, the difference between 3% on-cost (which was the initial British thought) and a 12% charge (that was discussed at one stage by the United States side) was a total of real significance to both sides. Both sides were able to produce arguments of substance, and precedents, to support their positions; but both were also aware that, as in the original Sales Agreement negotiations, a settlement had to be found. Finally, the positions were refined to a point where concessions on both sides could reasonably be made in support of a reasonable settlement, and it was agreed, and approved by ministers, that the United Kingdom would pay a surcharge of 7% on expenditure recorded after 31 December 1969, as a contribution towards the overheads and use of government facilities. Although this settlement did not remove all the outstanding financial problems likely to arise during the post-building period, it established a satisfactory basis for the continuation of financial and technical collaboration. These discussions were held on a separate basis from the complicated negotiations that developed in the same period over offsetting some of the dollar expenditures to which the Labour government had become committed with the Phantom, Hercules and F111K programmes; although it seems that, for accounting purposes, the dollar costs of POLARIS were brought into later defence agreements about the costs of the British Indian Ocean Territories development at Diego Garcia.(13)

The total estimated costs of the POLARIS programme, from December 1962 until the end of the financial year 1973–4, were approximately £520m.(14) This total includes running costs. The report in which this estimate is published identifies the cost of the four submarines as £162m (against the early estimates of £141m), and of purchasing missiles as £53m (against what was said to be the original estimate of £92m – a figure used in 1963 and subsequently reduced).(15) The costs of the Faslane Base, including Coulport, came out to £47m, and although in recent years the running costs of the completed force have risen substantially above the early estimates of £25m per annum, the rise is more due to inflation than to any inherent change in the scale of provision for either operating costs or refits. Even on the basis of the rather generalised public statements on costs, however, what we see is an estimate, made in 1964, of a gross cost, between 1963–4 and 1970–71, of £440m, and an eventual gross cost, for the period 1963–1974 of £520m; and the difference which, on the face of things, seems to be £80m for the longer period, has to take account of some £140m on running costs (although some of the costs for 1970–71 were included in the earlier estimate). The conclusion seems to be obvious that, even given the increases in submarine costs and the decreases in missile purchases, there was, overall, a significant saving on the programme, in the sense that it eventually took less money to produce and deploy the force than had originally been envisaged.

(13) See, for example, the report in *The Guardian*, 17 October 1975, p. 2.
(14) See Appendix 1, p. 37, of *The twelfth report from the Expenditure Committee, 1972–73, Nuclear Weapon Programme, HC.399*, July 1973.
(15) *Ibid*, p. vii.

CHAPTER SIX

The Joint Steering Task Group

The Joint Steering Task Group was set up as one of the obligatory mechanisms by which the POLARIS Sales Agreement would be managed; Article II of the Agreement identified the agencies to which each government delegated functional responsibility, established national Project Officers, and required them to meet together formally and periodically.(1)

The model for the JSTG was the Steering Task Group which the Special Projects Office had established in the American national programme; that was a committee composed of senior representatives from all the major naval and industrial organisations participating in the FBM programme, and had provided specialist sub-committees or panels through which many of the actual performance goals for the FBM system had been defined. The idea of including provision for a formal group of this sort in the Sales Agreement was put forward by Special Projects Office in January 1963, when the State Department was drawing up a draft document which might be the basis for detailed negotiations; Admiral Galatin and his advisers were by no means sure at that time quite what the burdens of co-operation would be but drawing on their experience they felt that there would be advantages in providing for a formal forum. Whether it would be a decision-making body or an advisory group, or something else, could not be foreseen. Admiral Mackenzie was immediately attracted to the concept; one of his strongest initial impressions of Special Projects Office was the pressure under which they were already working, and he – equally instinctively – felt that there would be advantages to his new organisation in being able periodically to meet SP's senior management. Accordingly there was very little discussion about the JSTG during the Sales Agreement negotiations, and no very clear idea of the function that it would perform; the draft wording of Article II was accepted virtually as it had stood initially.

---

(1) See Appendix 1 for the text of the Agreement.

As things turned out, the JSTG meetings came quite quickly to be regarded by both CPE and SP as very important, for nearly identical reasons. The periodicity was changed in 1965 from four times a year to three times a year, but throughout the initial building phase the meetings represented an opportunity, at set periods, to supplement and review a host of other meetings and activities. From Admiral Galatin's point of view, the meetings performed at least one of the tasks that the Steering Task Groups had usefully stimulated at the national level: whereas the STGs had encouraged new insights in FBM development goals by mixing scientists and engineers together, the JSTGs stimulated co-operation and co-ordination by mixing national managers.(2) But that was perhaps a bonus; for the two national Project Officers jointly, the JSTGs provided a discipline which was instrumental in maintaining a sense of urgency, and a high standard of work and preparation. Pressure was put on individuals and sections to complete matters of business, or at the very least to clarify their ideas and establish their positions. A JSTG did not supersede a specific problem or a particular negotiation; but it did provide a framework within which the most senior management personnel in the joint programme could be kept informed, could be made aware of any special difficulties, and could collectivise any problems or devices that gave rise to concern. In this way, the JSTGs functioned, in the joint programme, in something of the same way as the 'Monday morning meeting' did within SP. The benefit was heavily concentrated on the United Kingdom side insofar as it was much to CPE's advantage to have prescribed periods during which SP management was required to give full-time attention to problems which were invariably of more concern to the British; indeed, so evident was the pressure on SP during 1964–65 from the United States national programme (3) that Admiral Mackenzie thought it a constructive gesture to propose reducing the meetings to three a year. Although this suggestion was regretted by staff members in both organisations, whose own functions were assisted by quarterly instead of four-monthly meetings, it did quite materially relieve the load on Admiral Smith (who became Director of Special Projects in February 1965) and it emphasised the role of the JSTG as a supplemental and not a transcendental management tool.

The meetings fairly quickly developed a standard pattern; the respective Liaison Officers were nominally the joint secretaries of the Group, but the *de facto* management of the Group's business was organised by the senior civilian administrative staff in each organisation. By the third JSTG, in December 1963, a routine had been established: a provisional agenda was agreed about three weeks before the meeting, usually after an exchange of teleprinter messages between Washington and London, and position papers exchanged about a week beforehand. This was an

(2) Interview.
(3) Most notably arising from the overlap of the A3 building programme and the POSEIDON development project.

ideal, which was sometimes not attained; but if it had not been possible for one side or the other to prepare a paper for discussion, the reasons why, and an outline of the probable thrust of argument, were habitually available. The JSTG was not an adversarial forum, and was not the place to spring surprises. Meetings normally took place over a three-day period; on the morning of the first day the joint secretaries and their colleagues would meet to review the agenda and supporting documentation, and each national delegation would meet separately for briefing purposes. In the early afternoon there would be a plenary session, with the 'home team' Project Officer acting as Chairman. Although the specifically accredited members of the JSTG might total no more than twelve or fifteen, attendance at plenary sessions was usually more extensive, with staff officers and assistants attending not merely to hear the discussion but also to take part in any sub-committee work that had to take place. For the most part, discussion at the first plenary session tended to be limited to establishing what the current status of agenda items was, and what the JSTG could be expected to do about them. Some items recurred at regular intervals (e.g. the preparation of the Joint Annual Report to governments that was a requirement under the terms of the Sales Agreement) and some were more or less standard items (e.g. the review of the status of the Technical Arrangements); almost by definition the JSTG did not deal with critical or immediate problems, and certainly would not deal with them as an initial step towards control or resolution. There would usually be some items about which general discussion and comment would develop, but for the most part the Project Officers would delegate to specific groups, with specific (or at least definite) terms of reference, the job of evaluating the report, or the draft, or the intransigency, and reporting back by the second plenary session. The working groups would convene at once, and would use the middle day of the meeting as well to complete their work; the second plenary session would take place on the morning of the third day, to discuss the working group reports, agree the minutes of the first plenary session, and lay down any general requirements that might have emerged. The two Project Officers would not normally take part in any of the sub-committees; they might go off together to visit a specific facility, like one of the shipyards, or they might simply take the opportunity to talk to each other.

The collectivity which the JSTGs represented was an important, if largely accidental, device in developing and sustaining the sense of unity in the joint programme. Participation in an international programme was a consolidating element in SP's national status and reputation: association with SP was an important source of strength and *morale* to CPE, and to a very real extent the JSTGs represented the physical manifestation of these attributes. They also provided a framework for the social knowledge which each group had of the other. It was, of course, not an unbroken chain of friendliness, nor did it, for the most part, extend very far down the hierarchical structures. But, where it existed, it proved to be strong and durable: and the extent of the professional trust that was engendered, as well of the personal frienships, is a phenomenon of unusual strength.(4) The secretaries of the JSTG very early came to an agreement that there would be no competitive hospitality; rules did not allow it and common sense indicated that it was not necessary. There were however periodic formal entertainments, when the most senior staff, for example, were entertained to lunch by the Minister for the Navy; and regular informal entertainments too, paid for entirely, and sometimes catered, by the staff themselves, not so as to invoke comparison with the lavish contractor hospitality, which was a resilient myth and an evasive reality, but to offer a welcome to a friendly and well-regarded group of colleagues.

(4) It is, of course, difficult to judge the dependability of recollections fostered by interviews: but the persistence of comments, internal evidence in the files, and experience derived from other investigations, leaves little doubt about the reality of 'the POLARIS bond' for those who experienced it.

CHAPTER SEVEN

Shipyard Progress

The choice of the Vickers Shipbuilding Group yard at Barrow-in-Furness as the lead yard was announced publicly in the Estimates Debate on 11 March 1963. Cammell Laird of Birkenhead was the only serious contender, as it turned out, for the contract to build two other POLARIS submarines. The lead yard concept was necessary for three reasons. It facilitated the close liaison that would be necessary with the United States programme; it was an economical way to provide the range of planning services that would be necessary, and which Cammell Laird themselves could not in any event provide; and it obviated any requirement to provide additional planning resources from the Admiralty. The award of contracts was announced on 8 May(1) and both shipbuilders embarked on a task which involved an expansion of facilities, an increase in staff, a change in the structure of staffing, and a profound impact on the standards of work and the nature of management operations.

By the end of May 1963 it had been decided too that CPE should assume responsibility for the progressing of the construction programme of hunter-killer submarines. Vickers were the only shipbuilders with experience of nuclear submarine work; they had constructed DREAD-NOUGHT, were in the process of building VALIANT, and were scheduled to produce WARSPITE. The relationship between the POLARIS programme and the hunter-killer programme was therefore substantial. This interdependence was evident not only in the shipyards. VALIANT was to be powered by the first British reactor unit, then only at the prototype stage at Dounreay, but the design was to be used in the propulsion unit for the POLARIS submarines also. The delay which would occur in the laying-down of additional hunter-killer submarines, and about which so much of the Navy's initial reservations about POLARIS were centred, was evidence of the close connexion between the programmes; but it was the only direct impact of POLARIS work on other naval construction schedules and would be reduced in its effects by a slight acceleration in the lay-down rate in later years.(2)

---

(1) *The Times*, 9 May 1963.
(2) See *House of Commons Debates*, Vol. 675, Cols. 1255–56, 10 April 1963.

Shipyard facilities

The expansion of shipyard facilities and increases in the skilled and semi-skilled work forces there and elsewhere were the immediate problems which pre-occupied the shipbuilders through to mid-1964 and prompted some progress chasing by CPE, involving a visit by Admiral Mackenzie to all the major contractors towards the end of 1963.(3) Skilled manpower was at a premium, and welders and draughtsmen especially were in short supply. At Vickers, recruitment figures were monitored weekly in the early period and advantage was taken of a recession on the Clyde and in Dumbarton, which released some of the necessary trades, to undertake recruiting drives.(4) Between 1963 and 1967 the size of the work force at Vickers increased by approximately 45%.(5)

In early 1962, Cammell Laird had completed the first stage of an extensive shipyard reconstruction programme,(6) but further work costing £1.6 million was necessary to equip the yard for building POLARIS submarines. Moreover almost all of this investment had to be turned into physical structures and equipments in the first eighteen months of the POLARIS project. A high level welding shop was most urgently required so that prefabrication work on the first of the Company's submarines could be begun as quickly as possible. Reconstruction of two berths and a jetty, together with associated work to the road, drainage and river wall were next in order of priority.(7) The Vickers yard at Barrow also required additional facilities, and more extensive dredging of the Walney Channel.

The nature of the task in hand, constructing nuclear powered submarines and equipping them with a POLARIS weapon system, combined with the urgency and priority accorded to the programme to generate a widespread innovatory impulse in the building yards. It was reflected not only in managerial and organisational improvements but in technical progress in, for example, the development of advanced welding techniques.(8) Urgency and the size of the undertaking were reflected at the outset, in the rapid expansion of facilities and of the labour forces. However, the various organisational and procedural innovations associated with the building of the ship, the installation of the propulsion unit and weapon system, and the testing and tuning required before the whole system was commissioned, were reflected in the establishment of new planning controls and new quality control and assurance procedures.

(3) Interview.
(4) Interviews. William Denny and Brothers, of Dumbarton, and William Hamilton and Co., Port Glasgow, closed their yards during the period. See the *Shipbuilding Inquiry Committee, 1965–1966*, Cmnd, 2937, 1966, Appendix M, P 186 (The Gesses Report).
(5) See, "The Polaris Submarine Programme", *Nuclear Energy*, Nov–Dec 1967 p. 169. The increase was from 3,100 to 4,500.
(6) See "Modernization at Cammell Laird", *Welding and Metal Fabrication*, 31st July 1963, p. 283.
(7) See W. E. Armstrong and M. J. Freazey, "Shipyard Reconstructed for Polaris Submarines", *The Dock and Harbour Authority*, Vol. XLVIII, No. 569, March 1968, pp. 359–61.
(8) J. W. Wealleans and B. Allen, "Towards automating the Tig Welding Process", *Welding and Metal Fabrication*, Vol. 34, March 1969.

New planning offices were necessary to deal with the problems of co-ordination and time schedules, and to manage new standardised progress reporting methods both within the yards and to CPE that were required under the provision of the Admiralty contracts.(9) The scale of the quality control and assurance effort that developed was perhaps the most formative and pervasive feature of the changes brought about in the shipyards, especially at Barrow.

Quality control

In principle this was not an entirely novel development. Quality control was a standard feature of most productive processes and was an extremely important and integral part of nuclear engineering work, and safety in general. Significant advances had been achieved in the DREAD-NOUGHT programme where the new demands and circumstances associated with employing nuclear propulsion in a submarine had already been grappled with.(10) These advances, and the experiences gained, were to be carried over into the POLARIS programme where they were applied more extensively and with a different order of intensity.

The Technical Directorate at Bath was the single most important source, within the programme, of the insistence that the shipbuilders should take over the responsibility for weapon system testing and tuning and for providing the appropriately documented assurances of the consistency and quality of their product. It was also the fact that a basic practical need existed to employ techniques which were as far as possible compatible with those employed in the United States project, and which would ensure that the United Kingdom programme achieved standards and specifications comparable to those laid down in the Special Projects Office. Beyond this, and equally important as far as CPE was concerned, was the need to operate and to be seen to operate at a level of competence which would meet and perhaps exceed SP's expectations. It was this sort of additional appreciation that was instrumental in helping to establish for the most crucial linkage in the United Kingdom programme a cordially competitive, and highly productive, relationship.

In wider organisational terms, the Admiralty too was increasingly concerned to apply the general principle that the shipbuilder should be responsible for the quality of his own and his sub-contractors' product. Production and inspection are two potentially conflicting functions. The Admiralty had provided an independent service by employing Naval Overseers in the shipyards. In effect it was a 'cheap inspection service' and quality control service for the shipbuilders.(11) There had up to that time been a measure of operational co-ordination between the various

(9) Interviews.
(10) Interview.
(11) H. J. Tabb and S. A. T. Warren, "Quality Control Applied to Nuclear Submarine Construction", *Royal Institute of Naval Architects Quarterly Transactions*, Vol. 105, July 1966.

overseers but no specific direction or cohesion existed. The link between overseers and their headquarters departments had been particularly strong, sometimes stressing professional issues above Admiralty interests as a whole. The increased burden and particular demands of the quality control function associated with nuclear submarine construction had already, with the DREADNOUGHT programme, instituted proposals for a re-organisation of the overseeing service in the shipyards; with the advent of the POLARIS tasks, these changes were implemented, giving cohesion, and the opportunity to play a more effective role, to the overseeing service.(12) It was also increasingly evident that this developing and growing task would have to be shared by the shipbuilders.

A number of factors made quality control a distinctive aspect of the construction task. The increased diving depths and higher underwater speeds attained by nuclear submarines posed two sorts of difficulties; to keep the hull weight within reasonable limits at greater depths involved the use of stronger steels, which in turn meant much closer control of fabrication and welding procedures as well as improved inspection techniques. In this way the safety of the watertight envelope could be assured. High underwater speeds increased the risks associated with errors or control system failures, and this again required higher levels of quality control in building and installation.(13)

Shipbuilding is, literally, a 'dirty' business and general standards both of cleanliness and precision were at odds with the more precise requirements of nuclear engineering. The transition to DREADNOUGHT had meant working within reduced clearances and to very close tolerances. These features were even more significant in the POLARIS submarines where precise missile tube alignment was an additional requirement. Cleanliness in the building and installation processes therefore became an even more important aspect of quality control.(14) Moreover the special deterrent role of the POLARIS submarines presented additional demands; the highest standards and assurances of operational availability and reliability were required. Precise and standardised documentary evidence was needed to establish that inspections and tests had been carried out to the quality level specified and so provide those assurances, in the ship systems, as well as in the weapon system.

Consequently the production schedule was of prime significance in determining both physical progress and quality: the risk of dislocation of a time schedule could be minimised by adherence to effective quality control and assurance procedures. Time lost through unexpected failures of a system or piece of equipment could often be totally out of proportion to the inherent significance of the defect, and experience gained in the United States had strongly suggested that efficient quality control produced higher rates of success the first time a system was tested.(15) The

(12) Interview.
(13) Tabb and Warren, *op. cit.*
(14) Interview.
(15) Tabb and Warren, *op. cit.*

substantive philosophy underpinning the quality control and assurance effort in the United Kingdom POLARIS programme was epitomised by the Technical Director:–

"A proper programme is one that gives ample time at the end for testing, tuning and trials; ample time at the beginning for quality testing and for failures, and a few simple milestones in the middle."(16)

One-third of the total elapsed time between the order and the completion of the first POLARIS submarine was devoted to testing, tuning and trials: it was evident that if a part malfunctioned on the day before final acceptance the target date would not be met. Meeting such targets, and having it generally known and accepted that such targets must be met was an integral part of the operation and style of the programme, openly propagated and promoted by its directors. Although 'getting it right first time' was an ideal (a new device was 'bound to be wrong'), quality control was regarded as generating improvement through controlled and documented failure. Testing and inspection was a procedure for identifying troubles as early as possible; documentation of the tests established and recorded a learning process:

"if a part failed on RESOLUTION, you might catch it out on RENOWN."(17)

The contractual obligations which the shipbuilders were required to assume gave the first public indication that the novelty of the POLARIS task would materially affect standard practices. For the first time in the United Kingdom a naval ship contract required the shipbuilders to set up quality control organisations independent of the production process and the reorganised Admiralty overseeing service was available in the yards to monitor the constructors' performance. The Principal Naval Overseer now existed to act as the focal point of contact between the shipbuilders and the Admiralty; he was supported by the Naval Constructor Overseer, the Naval Engineer Overseer, the Naval Electrical Engineer (Nuclear), the Warship Weapons Overseer, and in addition for the POLARIS programme a Naval POLARIS Weapon Overseer. These officers were technically responsible in their own fields and the Principal Naval Overseer was responsible for co-ordinating the inspection service they provided and the efficiency with which it was performed.

The POLARIS Technical Directorate was drawn in to assist in the establishment of the shipyard quality control organisations in both shipyards, and to guide the drawing up and implementation of the appropriate procedures. A quality control working party consisting of hull,

(16) Interview: see also Mr. Baker's comments in the discussion accompanying the paper given by Tabb and Warren to the R.I.N.A., *op. cit.*
(17) Interview.

mechanical and electrical engineers was set up by the Technical Director to help identify the areas and systems to which quality assurance procedures were to be applied and to establish the form of documentary evidence which was to be required. As the quality control organisations were built up, so their responsibilities were extended. Initially it was decided to employ in each yard the available and relatively limited resources to provide assurance of quality in critical areas. The first task therefore entailed a review of the submarine design to select the structures, fittings and equipments which were vital to submarine safety. The impulse to classify too many items as critical was evident and had to be resisted so that the new organisations were not overloaded. A similar impulse to set standards which were unattainable in practice was also a general problem. Careful professional judgement was required, not only to identify and specify realistic governors, but also to appreciate that a high rate of delinquency associated with unattainable standards would exacerbate the difficulties involved in introducing these innovations, undermine their utility and limit the purpose they could serve.(18)

It was not until mid-1964 that the new quality control departments began to build up at Barrow and Birkenhead. The delay was caused, in part, by the preliminary work of elucidating what was necessary, and in part, by the obligation to give priority at the beginning of the programme to the immediate difficulties associated with the yard expansion. Only later could staff be recruited into the shipyards to establish the new departments. There was some organisational inertia too in an industry not generally regarded for its innovatory character; it was perhaps the more understandable since these particular innovations were an additional cost and involved a fundamental re-organisation of the structure of work in the shipyards. Fears were expressed about future commercial viability once the impact of the changes had been accommodated and the resources demanded by them had been committed.(19) In this context the uncertain political climate which surrounded the programme in 1964 had an impact too. Nobody on the contractors' side was enthusiastic about building up particular sorts of facilities and labour force levels with which they could have been stranded, had a new government cancelled the programme or seriously limited its size and scope.(20)

Clearly it was necessary to define carefully the limits of the effort to be put into quality control. The cost of quality assurance for key products in the aerospace industry, for example, could be considerably higher than the production costs of the item. It was some time before an organisation for quality control and assurance which represented approximately 8% of

(18) Tabb and Warren, op. cit.
(19) See, "RESOLUTION, First Polaris Missile Submarine for the Royal Navy"; Shipbuilding and Shipping Record, 19 October 1967, p. 547; and the comments of shipyard management staff in the discussion accompanying the paper given by Tabb and Warren to the R.I.N.A., op. cit.
(20) Interview.

the direct production labour force came to be regarded as an acceptable and appropriate indicator of the effort required.(21)

This measure of initial 'diffidence' was however overcome once the future of the programme was assured. The requirement was unassailable in principle; there was evidently too some potential commercial spin-off in generally improving product quality control; and in any event the Admiralty paid for the changes as a direct production charge. More particularly, the participation of Rolls Royce and Associates materially affected the shipbuilders' development and performance in this area. Rolls Royce and Associates had been responsible to the Admiralty for the provision and assurance of quality of the major proportion of nuclear equipment on the DREADNOUGHT project. They had to be satisfied also that installation of nuclear plant and mechanical systems by the main machinery contractor was according to specification, and that the records of quality were sufficient to assure the customer. This range of responsibilities was carried over to POLARIS work. On the other hand, the shipbuilders' responsibilities in this field on DREADNOUGHT had been confined to electrical installation work and agreeing with Rolls Royce and Associates that measures taken to ensure conformance to specification of the steam raising plant were adequate.(22) Consequently although the shipbuilders' attitudes initially to a radical increase in these responsibilities was rather tentative and their experience was relatively limited, it was effectively improved by the example and willingness of Rolls Royce and Associates and the wider experience which that firm had.

In the shipyards the creation of centralised quality control departments was formed by drawing together personnel already engaged on inspection (at Vickers it was 20 people), by transferring managers within the yards, and by recruiting qualified professional staff from industry. An Admiralty requirement that the Quality Control Manager should be directly responsible to the Shipyard Director and not report to him through the production organisation elaborated the contractual requirements designed to ensure objectivity and independent control. The preference was also expressed for a functionally organised quality control department, since many of the facets of quality extended through tasks common to hull, electrical and engineering departments. Common specifications for receipt and inspection of equipment and materials as well as standard formats for reports and other control procedures were introduced as essential and integral features of the developing control organisations.(23)

These new requirements, together with the expanded planning and testing organisations associated with POLARIS work, radically altered the structure of the work forces in the shipyards. This was especially true

(21) Tabb and Warren, *op. cit.*
(22) *ibid.*
(23) Tabb and Warren, *op. cit.*; E. H. Hunter, "Quality Control for a POLARIS Submarine", *Welding and Metal Fabrication*, Vol. 35, November 1967; "The POLARIS Submarine Programme", *Nuclear Energy*.

at Barrow where the ratio of qualified to unqualified staff rose from 1:5 (which compared favourably with average for shipbuilding of 1:10), to 2.5:4.(24) That is, between 1963 and 1967 the number of staff supporting the work force rose from 800 to 2,400. The quality control department at Vickers eventually consisted of 200 people and at least half of these were new recruits. At Cammell Laird, greater recruitment problems meant that by mid-1966 only 60% of the total need for their department had been achieved. But this still meant that they were operating an organisation which consisted of approximately 90 people.(25)

At the beginning, assurance procedures were confined to critical aspects of shipyard work and to keeping defective material out of the yards. The quality control of equipment and material supplied to a shipyard is such a vast undertaking that, effectively, the yard has to rely on the manufacturers to ensure good standards. But, just as responsibility for quality had passed from the overseeing service and was monitored through the application of standardised and documented reporting procedures by the shipbuilders, so two similar sorts of innovations were introduced to monitor the quality of equipment and materials provided for POLARIS work. The first of these were manufacturers' test forms that were to be used for significant items. They required the manufacturer to submit a schedule of tests for Admiralty approval, having first agreed them with local overseers; reports were then furnished on completion of tests. In this way a form of procedural audit was carried out. Secondly, for particularly important sub-contracts, the shipbuilders and the Polaris Executive collaborated in providing field inspections and a review of purchase orders, to check that the correct design drawings and specifications were referenced and that test and inspection requirements were clearly stipulated. Experience gained, in the United States and in the United Kingdom, suggested strongly that keeping defective raw materials and finished equipment from getting into the shipyards paid good dividends in savings on costs and of time.(26)

Procedural innovations never by themselves guarantee results, and a considerable promotional effort was applied to the job of persuading the sub-contractors not only to accept, comply with and properly implement new procedures but also to produce goods on schedule. In February 1964, Admiral Mackenzie began a series of visits to sub-contractors which complemented his visits to all the main contractors conducted towards the end of 1963. In addition, direct contacts with sub-contractors were developed by the CPE organisation in London, especially when there was evident need for progress chasing.(27) This combination of measures produced good results. Sub-contractors were made aware, in a novel way, of the significance of the larger undertaking to which they were contributing and of its particular needs and demands. The shipyards reported a

(24) *The Economist*, 20 April 1968.
(25) See the discussion accompanying the paper given by Tabb and Warren to the R.I.N.A., *op. cit.*
(26) Tabb and Warren, *op. cit.*
(27) Interviews.

distinct improvement in sub-contractor reaction times and contractual performance which was instrumental in maintaining the impetus of deliveries, and of progress generally. The round of visits was not repeated, but its effect persisted and on several subsequent occasions, telephone calls were sufficient to regenerate awareness of the programme needs.(28)

By the autumn of 1965, extensive progress had been made in the application of quality assurance to crucial areas, and an extension of requirements to other areas was begun. Past experience indicated which processes, systems and equipment were persistently troublesome and which were significant although perhaps not critical to safety and performance. Controlled items and quality requirements were not immutably fixed but subject to a continuing learning process, and to the adaptive relationship between the shipyards and C P E, which mediated the developing needs of the programme.

Two features which fundamentally complemented the quality control effort were not integrated into the new quality control departments. These were the Dockside Test Organisation and the Calibration Organisation. A competent organisation for testing equipment after installation was essential for considerations of safety as well as performance. One had been established when the Admiralty purchased the nuclear equipment for DREADNOUGHT and it developed into a testing unit for the submarine as a whole as well as its sub-systems. This organisation was retained intact for the POLARIS project and became responsible for the overall administrative direction, co-ordination and documentation of the testing of all ship items prior to acceptance, and for the preparation of test forms to be approved by the POLARIS Technical Directorate. In addition, it organised, programmed and executed all the test operations: recorded and evaluated the data and certified the tests. The unit consisted of five test groups comprising representatives of the shipbuilders, Naval Overseers and appropriate contractors (see Tables 1 and 2).

Table 1 – Dockside Test Organisation

Test group	Test and trials responsibilities
1. REACTOR	Nuclear plant and its containment
2. SHIP	All systems not part of reactor plant, propulsion machinery, or weapon equipment
3. PROPULSION	Propulsion plant and associated equipment
4. TACTICAL WEAPONS	All weapon systems with the exception of the Ballistic Missile System
5. POLARIS WEAPON	Ballistic Missile System

Note: Compiled from Tabb and Warren, "Quality Control Applied to Nuclear Submarine Construction".

(28) Interviews.

81

Table 2 – Polaris Weapon System, Sub-systems and Contractors

Sub-system	Contractors
1. NAVIGATION SYSTEM	Elliott/Sperry
2. FIRE CONTROL SYSTEM	GEC and BAC
3. MISSILE	BAC
4. LAUNCHER TUBE CONTROL SYSTEM	Vickers launcher group
5. TEST INSTRUMENTATION SYSTEM	GEC and BAC

Note: Compiled from interviews and from Captain C. W. H. Shepherd "The UK Polaris Project", *Journal of The Royal Aeronautical Society*, Vol. 70, September 1966.

Approximately 100 test engineers were involved in work on the non-POLARIS area. The POLARIS Weapon System Test Group itself comprised 120 engineers with between 50 and 60 technical and clerical support staff. It was a composite group, which combined engineers from contractors in the United Kingdom and United States, each concerned with a separate sub-system as well as with the test procedures as a whole. Vicker's Chief Test Engineer co-ordinated the group and was responsible for the complete testing of the POLARIS weapon system (see Table 2).

Calibration

Special Projects Office took an early opportunity in discussions about construction techniques and procedures to urge that CPE should establish particular arrangements in their programme for the control of measurement and accuracy. United States experience on a number of large-scale and sophisticated technological projects had shown that such programmes frequently suffered because inaccurate and inconsistent measurements had led to wrong conclusions about the performance and behaviour of systems and equipment. Advanced mechanical, optical and electronic concepts and equipment employed in the POLARIS system required much higher levels of accuracy, and much stricter controls over test equipment than current procedures had allowed for. Accordingly, a section of the Technical Arrangements was agreed, to establish agreed standards and procedures for calibration control, and as a result, the calibration facility that was built up at Barrow between 1964–66 was designed to provide measurement of a wide range of parameters, and to establish standards of measurement and accuracy which were to be applied to the installation tests and inspections. The calibration laboratory provided a service, as part of the lead yard concept, to Cammell Laird also and in addition supported the construction and operation of the RNPS at Faslane. Senior management and technical personnel were trained in the United States to establish and operate the facility while United States advisers assisted in the establishment and operation of the facility in Barrow.(29)

Two features associated with all of these changes need to be emphasised. The first is that the programme did not progress without any difficulty or mishap because they had been instituted. Secondly, their utility was not always, and sometimes not primarily, related simply to the control function they were intended to perform.

General progress

The measures did establish a quality control complex, but the implementation of its procedures was not always what it should have been and there were gaps in its operation.(30) Just as quality control derived in large part from the experiences on DREADNOUGHT, so its problems there were carried over into POLARIS work. This was evident in the difficulties associated with the quality of the high tensile steel used in the building process, the quality of welding and the hair-line cracks which developed in the nuclear submarines in which the steel had been used – including RESOLUTION. The presence of such cracks was acknowledged in August 1965 after they had been discovered on DREADNOUGHT.(31) British steel in use at that time included small elements of non-metallic inclusions which had not previously been thought significant but which did affect the steel's capacity to withstand the additional strain imposed on it by the rigours of nuclear submarine performance. In this instance the steel industry had produced the steel to specification (QT 35) but experience found the specification inadequate and it had to be revised.(32)

Problems were experienced both in raising the specification and in acquiring the required amounts of a better steel. Nuclear submarine steel was not generally regarded as a basis from which to develop production at a commercial rate and find additional markets, although later it was reported that some commercial benefit did result from the improvements

(29) See "The Polaris Submarine Programme", *Nuclear Energy*; and "RESOLUTION, First Polaris Missile Submarine for the Royal Navy", *Shipbuilding and Shipping Record*, 19 September 1967, p. 548.
(30) Interviews.
(31) See *The Times*, 22 August and 10 November 1965; also Interview.
(32) See *The Times*, 10 August and 23 September 1966. The problems associated with welding and steel quality appeared first in the components of the nuclear propulsion plant at Dounreay, and assistance in getting supplies of adequate stainless steel to replace specialised components was sought and obtained from Admiral Rickover's office in January 1964 and again in 1966. The steel problems relating to hull fabrication first began to be troublesome in early 1964, when emergency measures had to be taken to procure sufficient supplies of molybdenum for the steel mills. The discovery of hairline cracks in DREAD-NOUGHT led to rigorous surveys and tests on all the other submarine hulls, completed and building, and, naturally, to a good deal of public enquiry and concern. Reassurance was given that 'such cracks are normal in heavy welded constructions of this sort; they introduce no risk to the submarine or her crew. However, their repair does require extra heavy work at routine docking or refit periods'. (See, for example, the report in the *St. Louis POST-DISPATCH*, 25 September 1966.)

required for such work.(33) Steel made in the United States to a comparable specification (HY 80) was fairly readily available, and proved to be of good quality: sufficient quantities were bought in to complete the hull fabrication of all four POLARIS boats (and later, to build hunter-killer hulls). The decision to use United States steel was announced in August 1966, and the extra cost amounted to £1.15m by November of that year.(34)

A number of other factors combined to create delays to or threaten the progress of the programme throughout the 1964–66 period. In 1964 and 1965, the heavy demands on resources brought about by the conjunction of the hunter-killer and POLARIS submarine work were particularly evident. Construction work on the second SSN, VALIANT, was well underway in January 1963 and the commitment to a third, WARSPITE, had been made, and work had begun. Although this meant that Vickers at Barrow had accumulated a good deal of practical experience, only one nuclear submarine was yet at sea, and the new British propulsion design was not yet proved. The work load induced by running the two programmes in parallel was inevitably going to be very difficult to manage.

During 1964, the maintenance of the impetus that was necessary to complete the POLARIS submarines to time became more and more difficult as the continuation of the programme itself became – or seemed to become – a political issue. In one sense, the debate which led up to the General Election was a stimulus to action: the further ahead the programme got, the less feasible it would become for any new government to abandon it. In another sense, the mere fact that the programme was a matter of contention made it more difficult to persuade contractors to extend their liabilities.(35) One of the proposals considered was to stop work on WARSPITE and stand it over, until the POLARIS work was completed. But this proposal was resisted strongly in CPE. The idea had some attraction, but it would enormously complicate the work-loadings at Barrow, and might well have a bad effect on the POLARIS programme generally. The recovery of slippages, and successful completion of WARSPITE, without material effect on the POLARIS schedules, became an issue which provided the project organisation with an opportunity to consolidate its reputation and demonstrate its determination to maintain original commitments and targets. CPE was firm in the opinion that if WARSPITE was to go then it would in effect constitute evidence to suggest that the organisation was 'as malleable as anybody else'.(36) It was the propagation of entirely the opposite perception that was inherent in the promotional style of CPE and integral to the successful achievement of its purpose. WARSPITE stayed, was commissioned in April 1967 and was quickly followed by RESOLUTION in October, a time schedule

(33) Interview: *The Economist*, 20 April 1968.
(34) *House of Commons Debates*, Vol. 737, Col. 75, 29 November 1966.
(35) Interview.
(36) Interview.

which involved 1¾ commissioning teams being assembled at Vickers to cope with the work load.(37)

At Cammell Laird, their first SSBN was three months behind schedule when launched in February 1967, although opportunity had been taken to do extra work while the hull was still on the slip. As a company Cammell Laird had not had the experience in nuclear submarine work which Vickers had acquired and their learning phase coincided with the restricted time scale of the POLARIS submarine schedules. It was also a learning process which applied most to management, and which the lead yard concept was designed in part to facilitate. Initial difficulties were concerned with building up the facilities and shipyard equipment, a process which was not advanced by a shipwrights' strike from March to June 1964 (see Table 4). The award to Cammell Laird of a contract to build a hunter-killer submarine in August 1966 provided employment for a pool of skilled labour which could be re-assigned according to the variable work loadings of the POLARIS task. But, although the firm addressed itself 'maturely' to the problems of management and organisation their performance was consistently behind that of Vickers (between 10–13 months, see Table 3), and in January 1967 involved some high level progress chasing and 'blunt speaking' by Mr. Roy Mason, then the Minister of Defence for Equipment.(38)

It was recognised at the outset that the relationship between Vickers and Cammell Laird would be a likely source of problems. But in operation it was not a uniformly difficult one. At individual working levels, co-operation was reasonably good and appreciation of respective performances was favourable. At more senior levels, however, the formal institutional and commercial status of, and relationship between, the two shipbuilders did seem to inhibit any permanent or enthusiastic co-operation. In addition, procedures which operated well at working departmental levels tended to exacerbate institutional sensitivities at senior managerial levels. Frankness in team reporting and discussion paid dividends at one level but were a potential source of friction at the institutional level. The process of formally reporting difficulties to CPE, while providing a useful mechanism for resolving problems and questions of priority, also tended to formalise and institutionalise issue between the two yards.(39)

Labour relations at Vickers over which there had been some difficulty in 1964 deteriorated sharply in 1968, and culminated in an inter-union dispute about pipe-fitting and testing (see Table 4). By December 90% of the work force was affected. The preoccupation in CPE, following the completion of REPULSE in September and the organisation's wider remit for SSN construction, was as much related to the reliability of the yard in general for naval construction purposes as it was with ensuring the timely completion of the remaining POLARIS work. It was not until

(37) Interview.
(38) Interviews. See also *The Times*, 31 January 1967.
(39) Interviews.

February 1969 that a board of inquiry was established and the inter-union dispute resolved.(40)

Table 3 – SSBNs: Shipbuilder Work Months

SSBN	Builder	To Launch	To Completion	Total
RESOLUTION	Vickers	32	13	45
RENOWN	Cammell Laird	33	22	55
REPULSE	Vickers	33	10	43
REVENGE	Cammell Laird	35	21	56

Table 4 – Principal Stoppages at Barrow and Birkenhead for the 5 years ending 31 December 1968 (5,000 or more working days lost)

Area	Date of Stoppage	Number of Workers Involved	Number of Working Days Lost	Cause or Object
Birkenhead	16.3.64 to 5.6.64	1,260	54,000	Claim by shipwrights for a wage increase of 1s per hour.
Barrow	13.7.64 to 20.10.64	135	7,900	In support of a claim for an increase in wages.
	5.6.68 to 3.12.68	420	39,800	Protest by apprentices against the introduction of a new pay structure.
	1.7.68 to 12.7.68	920	7,200	In support of a claim for parity in repair allowances.
	3.7.68 still in progress at the end of 1968.	1,845	166,000	Inter-union demarcation dispute over allocation of certain work.
	9.9.68 still in progress at the end of 1968.	70	5,400	In support of fitters and apprentices already in dispute (see above).

SOURCE: House of Commons Debates, Vol. 778, 26 February 1969, Columns 323–324.

The managers and contractors in defence programmes had become accustomed over the years to work falling behind schedule and to revisions of programme plans that accepted delays as ineluctable. Work fell behind time in the POLARIS programme and schedules had to be

(40) See The Times for 4 October and 16 December 1968 and 26 February 1969.

reshaped but the original and most significant objective was adhered to and achieved – RESOLUTION and the rest of the squadron deployed operationally on time. Keel-laying, launching and other target dates were general indicators of progress but what they represented could alter substantially, depending on the installation and testing that went on between these milestones.(41) Although there was no complacency about missing any one of these target dates, given that CPE was sensitive to the impact it would have on the promotional effort required to emphasise the urgency and priority of the programme, a commitment to a recovery philosophy was instrumental in ensuring that work loss was made up and that the distinctiveness of the operation was maintained. In addition, POLARIS work at the shipyards was essentially a production task and this feature partially facilitated the problem of rescheduling the work and directing resources into lagging areas to effect recovery. For example, although RENOWN was on the slipway longer than she ought to have been, a limited amount of work was put in progress that would normally have been started once the submarine was launched. It was also at this level, and with this sort of problem, that the instrumental utility of certain managerial devices was demonstrated. PERT networks, for example, were used in this way to good effect when delays to WARS-PITE's progress gave concern, in 1964/65. They were especially useful in planning the work necessary to restore progress by identifying whence to divert effort and where to apply it with best effect without disproportionately and adversely affecting general progress.(42)

Throughout the latter part of the construction phase, from 1965–66 onwards, maintaining progress in the shipyards remained a continuing and demanding task, if a less exciting one than beginning construction had been. Individual problems threatened the progress of the programme, such as labour difficulties, strikes and the accidental flooding of compartments in RENOWN while she was fitting out. These generally required the re-ordering of schedules, the adaptation of plans and redistribution of resources, so as to maintain momentum and stay within reach of the original targets.

There were in addition, however, more general sorts of difficulties associated with the shift in the construction process from hull fabrication to fitting out the submarines, installing equipment, and testing and tuning the various sub-systems. Work on these tasks presented new planning requirements and new planning problems which frequently demanded the day-to-day specification of tasks and planning of work. In this sense, therefore, the advancement of the work in the shipyards never became an automatic function. Instead it had to adapt constantly to special problems, shifting general requirements and variable rates of progress at different times in different areas. Recovery programmes of various kinds were regularly required to maintain overall progress.

(41) See the comments in *The Times*, 27 April 1966, reporting that work on RESOLUTION and RENOWN was behind schedule.
(42) Interview.

RESOLUTION was commissioned on 2 October 1967 (to be followed at intervals by the other SSBNs, see Table 5), conducted her first missile firings in a demonstration and shakedown operation (DASO) during February and March of 1968, and was on operational patrol by June of that year.(43)

Table 5 – Principal Milestones

SSBN in Order of Acceptance (anticipated 1963)	Laid Down	Launched	Accepted
RESOLUTION (Vickers)	22.2.64	15.9.66	2.10.67 First
RENOWN (Lairds)	25.6.64	25.2.67	15.11.68 Third
REPULSE (Vickers)	12.3.65	4.12.67	29.9.68 Second
REVENGE (Lairds)	19.6.65	15.3.68	4.12.69 Fourth

This event signalled the beginning of the end of the construction task. Although the last SSBN was not to become operational until 1970 the headquarters manpower effort had progressively to be re-deployed to support, maintenance and refit tasks. In accord with this change of emphasis the post of Chief Polaris Executive was abolished in June 1968 and replaced by a new two star appointment with the title of Assistant Controller (Polaris).(44) AC(P) was to exercise the residual functions of CPE until the SSBN construction programme was complete and he succeeded CPE as the United Kingdom's Project Officer under the terms of the Polaris Sales Agreement. He was to work under the joint superintendence of the Controller of the Navy, and the Chief of Fleet Support, whose responsibilities included the oversight of the preparations for the refit of the POLARIS submarines.

The Technical Directorate in Bath was similarly reorganised. The Technical Director (Polaris) became the Director Project Team (Submarines) and his organisation remained as a project team. His responsibilities were essentially to be concerned with the drawing up of the 'work package' for each refit. Each 'work package' was to include full design information and documentation. The refits themselves were to be conducted by an integrated refit management team at Rosyth responsible to the Admiral Superintendent there, but subject to the executive authority of the Director General Dockyards and Maintenance. By June 1970 the first cycle of construction, acceptance, trials, operational patrol and refit was completed when RESOLUTION went to Rosyth for her first refit.(45)

(43) See *The Times,* 5th March and 21st June 1968.
(44) Later changed to Deputy Controller (Polaris), in consonance with other changes in the Controller of the Navy's supporting management structure.
(45) See *The Times,* 23 June 1970.

In general shipyard progress was characterised by retrieval and recovery. Such programmes operate directly, by changing the status of a delinquent area, injecting more resources into it, and paying particular attention to the resolution of its problems. But some more general philosophy of retrieval – that is to say a predisposition to adhere to milestones and to take special action if progress falters – must provide the impulse and general support for instituting and carrying out any particular programme of recovery. And such a philosophy is directly associated with the expectations that operate in a project concerning the standards of achievement and the degree of urgency required. If the standards of achievement and the degree of urgency in practice are high, and are expected to be high, there will be less disposition to tolerate short-falls in the progress of work. Within the shipyards work did not always and automatically progress according to schedule. What was distinctive about the project, however, was the disposition to pull progress back on to schedule by diverting resources and increasing effort as situations demanded.

This condition prevailed more generally throughout the POLARIS project. The managerial and procedural innovations associated with the project had a promotional significance as well as, on occasions, a direct instrumental utility in establishing that disposition, and confirming the associated expectations by providing a record of achievement. The relative novelty of these procedures defined and demonstrated the peculiar significance of the programme at an operational level, which the formal accreditation of priority was meant to convey at an official level. Where they were implemented and where they worked (and these areas were always more limited than their formal justifications allowed), they improved performance. But it is difficult to disassociate the usefulness of this specifically instrumental feature from the more general appearance of distinctive competence to which it contributed. Neither can it receive more acclaim than the utility and importance of that sense of cohesion, style and novel purpose, which the new POLARIS language of standardised reporting procedures and detailed documentation, systematically promoted throughout the programme, gave. It was these general characteristics that provided the means, and the record of substantive achievement, required for the promotional effort that was employed to motivate the nexus of relationships between the industrial organisations and government departments which, overall, constituted the programme in the United Kingdom.

CHAPTER EIGHT

The Base and the Support Facilities

The decision that specialised support facilities would be required for the POLARIS submarine squadron was taken at the first meeting of the Admiralty POLARIS Committee in February 1963. On the basis of information that had been made available by Special Projects Office about maintenance practices, and by the operational authorities in the United States Navy about operational cycles, the Committee reviewed the principles that should be used to plan the support and operational philosophy to be applied to the British force. Given the likely size of the force, it would be even more important than the Americans had found that the maximum operational availability should be achieved; this inferred manning each submarine with two crews and setting up closely controlled maintenance and refit schedules. In turn, this objective required the provision of material and manpower resources, for British as well as for American equipment, in sufficient and readily available quantities (and quality) to ensure that the schedules could not only be met but sustained, throughout the life of the force. It was clearly going to be a major task and lent support to the argument that the Polaris Executive should include a specialist logistics component as a part of the organisation.(1)

The task divided into four major parts. The first was to identify the necessary scales of stores and spare parts, and to make provision for them; this was, classically, the function of the Admiralty Supply departments, who allocated staff to CPE for this purpose. The second was to establish the scope of the facilities that would have to be set up: workshops, store-houses, power supplies, accommodation, communications and so on. As an organisational task this was less straightforward, insofar as it required the coordination of the efforts of a number of authorities, not only in other government departments like the Ministry of Aviation and the MPBW but in local government as well. It was in this area that the Polaris Logistics Officer and his immediate staff concentrated their activities. The third component was the planning of ship refits, including nuclear refuelling of the propulsion plant. In terms of timescale this requirement was less urgent than the others, though no

(1) See Chapter Four.

less important. And the fourth component was to ensure that all of these activities marched in step with the other tasks of the Polaris Executive.

By the end of March 1963, it had been decided that the operating base should be located at Faslane, where the Third Submarine Squadron already had a forward operating base, centred around jetty facilities and the submarine depot ship, HMS MAIDSTONE. The refit yard for the submarines was to be H.M. Dockyard, Rosyth, where extensions to the yard's capacity were already underway to enable HMS DREADNOUGHT and later hunter-killer submarines to be refitted. Later H.M. Dockyard, Chatham was equipped to provide a comparable range of services for the SSNs and Rosyth was reserved to the POLARIS Squadron.(2) Faslane had a number of desirable operational and safety characteristics which caused it to be preferred to other possible sites, including the immediate availability of government-owned land for the base itself and the armament depot which would need to be located close by. But, architecturally, it was not the easiest of sites to develop; the hills and the hardness of the rock (and, during the building phase, the high rainfall) gave rise to a number of persistent difficulties.

As in other areas of the programme, the logistic planning was beset by 'chicken and egg' difficulties. The urgency of the timescale to which CPE was to work called for early decisions to be made so that lengthy processes – like designing and building a large complex of buildings, in this instance, could be put in hand straight away. But they could not begin until sufficiently firm and detailed information was available to be sure that the initial plans were unlikely to require later, time-consuming, modifications. Detailed knowledge about the POLARIS weapon system was obviously going to take time to acquire and assimilate; but it was also going to be fairly difficult to make suitable assumptions at once about the maintenance load for the ship systems. DREADNOUGHT was at sea, and provided some experience on which to draw; but there was yet no extensive knowledge about the needs of the VALIANT class, on which the POLARIS submarine hull design was based, and no clear ideas about any special problems that would arise from the mating of the main weapon system to this design. So, early planning began by dealing with general issues: the organisation of the stores and spare parts network of sites at Copenacre, Eaglescliffe and Faslane itself, the general layout of an 'ideal type' base to identify highway, sewerage and power needs and, along with the rest of CPE, the acquisition of as much information as possible from SP.(3)

---

(2) These decisions were announced in April 1963 (*House of Commons Debates*, Vol. 676, Cols. 219–223, 24 April 1963) and March 1965 (*House of Commons Debates*, Vol. 708, Col. 665, 11 March 1965).
(3) Representatives from the Stores and Armament Supply departments were appointed to SPRN's staff in Washington: one was based full time at the Naval Weapons Annexe, Charleston, S. C., and another spent most of his time at the Lockheed company plants in California.

Stores and spare parts

The stock inventory for the POLARIS weapon system ran to rather more than 80,000 separate items and although usage and replenishment rates were well established for the A2 system, the position in regard to the A3 system was still undetermined for a number of components and equipments. It was not therefore a simple matter, either for installation in the submarines or for building up system spares, to determine what had to be procured. A separate contract had to be arranged between the Admiralty and the Electric Boat Company to provide the details of what ship-fitted equipments should be ordered to complete the hull installations, in addition to the contract that was negotiated between the Bureau of Ships and EB to provide installation and guidance drawings. The contract provided for the supply of components, materials and spares against orders placed by the Admiralty after the scrutiny of schedules and drawings and what were called 'group lists'. These were schedules of work units, defined in terms of what work actually took place in the process of installation, identified trade by trade. The schedules effectively replaced compartment or equipment plans as the production unit on which progress was based. The 'group master schedule' identified all Government Furnished Equipment (the US Navy equivalent of Admiralty Supply Items) and provided a check on material which might also be identified as necessary in PE-PLAN 'shopping lists'. The main flow of weapon system-linked and electrical components was programmed to build up through 1965, and the staff of the Technical Directorate worked very effectively together to define the full range of requirements by the middle of 1964; but the actual supply of the material fell behind schedule, as much as five months in some cases, and remained a major cause of concern in RESOLUTION's programme throughout the autumn and winter of 1965. A recovery programme was instituted, which resolved most of the shortfalls by the early months of 1966.

The provision of weapon system equipment parts proceeded more smoothly once the 'learning curve' of assimilation flattened out. The links between the PLO's staff and their equivalents in SP and at Charleston became close and fruitful, and the difficulties that arose from time to time on provisioning seldom reached major proportions. Agreement was reached in the autumn of 1964 about the principles on which arrangements for the return and repair of equipments to the United States should be based; because CPE was not provided with design information under the terms of the Sales Agreement, there would be a limit to the scope of any repairs that could be undertaken at Faslane. Although considerations of speed and economy pointed to the need to include a specialised workshop (the Module Repair Facility) at Faslane, on the model of similar workshops in US support facilities, some types of equipment would need, as in the United States programme, to be returned to the manufacturing agencies for repair, and for this type of item a system of joint replenishment was agreed. Later on, when the testing and tuning of equipment, initially in the training school at Faslane, began, the Department of Defense agreed that Faslane should be incorporated in the teletype communication system (AUTODIN) which allowed virtually instantaneous communication with the major United States Navy stock-handling depots. Similar communication links were set up between Faslane, Rosyth, Bath and the major Royal Navy store depots throughout the United Kingdom.

Missiles and missile spare parts

Early in the programme, there was a good deal of concern, at Board and ministerial level, to define responsibilities between the Admiralty and Ministry of Aviation clearly and definitively. Relationships between the two departments historically had not been easy and the Admiralty was, collectively, determined that the prospects of completing the POLARIS programme successfully should not be put at any additional hazard by any divided responsibility, or by any divided loyalty to the general naval cause which the new programme was seen to embody. The Navy suspected that Aviation's SKYBOLT scars would be long in the healing, and they had their own SEASLUG scars to display. The crux of the matter, for CPE's staff, was that the Admiralty should be the approval authority for the missile. The approval authority, in the government service, was responsible for assessing the suitability of a weapon for service use, both in regard to safety and to its operational characteristics; it specified the conditions under which the weapon might be used and it set the inspection and maintenance standards that should be followed. The circumstances of the Nassau Agreement, in which an existing system was to be procured, made the reservation of this responsibility to the Admiralty a logical consequence, although the design and provision of a suitable British 'front end' provided the Ministry of Aviation with a crucial role to play.

This was not, however, the only organisational difficulty. The determination of appropriate safety standards was an important, and potentially sensitive, area. The attitudes of the United States Navy and the Royal Navy towards safety controls had differed over the years and it was quite conceivable that the Inspectorate of Naval Ordnance, and the Ordnance Board, might require different procedures and standards to those which had been incorporated in the POLARIS designs and layouts. If there had to be differences, this in itself would be unwelcome to CPE, whose determination was to alter nothing that did not have to be altered; but it was even more important that alterations should not in any way degrade the operational characteristics of the proved system. To find out whether any changes would have this effect might take both time and money to establish, and to make the earliest possible resolution of this difficulty, an Inspector of Naval Ordnance was appointed to act as SPRN's local staff officer in the Lockheed Missile and Space Company's offices at Sunnyvale, California, in addition to the CINO designated staff in Bath. CINO's participation in the programme proved very helpful, both in regard to the deployed system, and in the establishment of safety procedures and controls at the RNAD, Coulport.

Coulport was some eleven miles by water and seven miles by land from Faslane; the armament depot, which would store torpedoes as well as missiles, would be the responsibility of the Director of Armament Supply. The planning of the depot had to provide for the care and maintenance of many technically complex equipments as well as for their storage, issue and replenishment; although the range of items was not nearly so great as on the Naval Stores side, their proper care was crucial and called, in addition to careful planning, for an extensive training programme in the United States for the technical staff who would be concerned in the operation of the depot.(4) Test and check-out equipment would need to be installed, and accurately regulated environmental controls would be necessary. Indeed, as time went on, it became apparent that it was the technical equipment controls and processes that presented the greatest difficulties. As in the case of the RN Polaris School there was no directly relevant American model upon which the design of the depot could be based in detail, although the new POLARIS Missile Facility, Pacific on Puget Sound, provided SP with precedents (and design experience) that were very helpful. The scale of the technical problems to be surmounted was daunting, and the difficult terrain at Coulport – steep gradients, hard rock and underground springs – was an added complication to the building of the depot.

There was however a fundamental organisational difficulty too. Although at the level of theory the dual nature of Coulport's role, combining technical as well as supply functions, was not unprecedented, the scale and the nature of the technical issues were novel to the Armament Supply Department. But DAS's management hierarchy was dominated by supply specialists and the status of the engineering staff was relatively low. Technical issues were not therefore grasped as firmly or as early as they might have been, and in spite of remedial action that was taken from time to time as the reported status of progress at Coulport dropped to an unsatisfactory level, the possibility that Coulport would not be ready in time to perform the full range of its defined duties for RESOLUTION's first patrol began to emerge as a distinct likelihood by the end of 1966. A recovery programme was instituted by the project Management Team, and additional support was arranged through the provision of Lockheed staff, as part of an augmented contract technical service programme agreed with SP, and through the provision of extra constructional and engineering resources. Much of the slippage was recovered in this way and the depot facilities were tested and checked-out in time for RESOLUTION. But the argument whether the depot should remain a DAS responsibility, or whether it should have more properly been regarded as a technical establishment – in which case it would have become

(4) The training programme was carried out between 1964–1966, principally at Charleston and Sunnyvale.

a Weapons Department responsibility – was a proper issue to raise, and had nothing to do with the skills or backgrounds of particular groups, who all worked with considerable diligence to procure a satisfactory outcome. It had to do rather more with the difficulty of fitting a novel function into a structure of defined responsibilities and organisations, and illustrated, more clearly perhaps than in any other part of the programme, that the powers of the Polaris Executive to assemble and deploy resources were as much limited by the structure of its component elements as by any financial or political guidelines.

Re-entry systems

The decision to base the BNBMS upon the A3 weapon system produced a requirement to design and provide a compatible British re-entry system. This was clearly a complex engineering task in itself, but it was also a sensitive political area, in which the exchange or provision of information was limited by agreements which pre-dated the POLARIS Sales Agreement, and which very carefully defined the procedures, as well as the scope, of any information-flow. Indeed, in almost all important particulars, the 1958 Exchange Agreement (which had been amended in 1959) rather than the Sales Agreement was the effective authority under which the Ministry of Aviation's team, under Admiral Dossor, went about their task in this area.(5) The United States authorities – which in this case were represented by a group staffed by officials of the Atomic Energy Commission under an SP chairman – were committed to provide the basic data whereby a British re-entry system could be mated to the rest of the missile, but precisely what data would be required, and whether the information could be supplemented by the provision of any hardware components, had to be worked out in careful detail, against the limits laid down by United States law as well as against the needs of the British design. A special committee, called the Joint Re-entry System Working Group, was set up to provide a forum for discussion and a channel by which information could be passed. By March 1964 a decision on the type of re-entry system to be provided was made by the United Kingdom side, and the JRSWG was reconstituted, with a slightly wider membership, to assist in the planning for the manufacture and support of the approved design. This required a defined division of responsibilities between the AEC and the Department of Defense about their respective roles, as well as the preparation of PEPLAN-type schedules of equipments and maintenance plans.

The proving of the design required a number of experimental tests, including an underground nuclear test, which was carried out at the AEC's testing ground in Nevada in November 1965, and was announced in the House of Commons on November 18. The Prime Minister told the

---

(5) *Agreement for Cooperation on the uses of Atomic Energy for Mutual Defence Purposes*, July 1958 (Cmmd. 537), HMSO London: Amended in 1959 (Cmnd. 859).

House that the test, which was in every way successful, "would lead to a very considerable saving in costs".(6) The design was completed in the spring of 1966, along with the definition of storage and maintenance parameters. Production was put in hand at once and, although some difficulties in maintaining progress were reported, a full set of re-entry systems was ready, as intended, for RESOLUTION's first operational patrol.

The Main Base

The design of the base facilities at Faslane was principally the responsibility of the Ministry of Public Buildings and Works, which absorbed the Directorate-General of Navy Works in April 1963. But the design had to meet the stated requirements of the user, which meant that besides the composite needs of C P E, the requirements of the Dockyard and Maintenance department, the personnel departments, and of the Flag Officer, Submarines had to be taken into account. They were all coordinated by the Polaris Logistics Officer, and this meant that his office became the clearing-house for all the plans and ideas that were thrown up, some of them in virtual ignorance in the early days of what the demands of operating the POLARIS force would entail. Although the Polaris School was contiguous to the Base, its planning was a separate activity, in which the P L O was concerned only in the bricks-and-mortar side at first, although the provision of accommodation for the staff and their families also became part of his concern. Indeed, married quarters, houses for key civilian personnel and service accommodation eventually became a major preoccupation, and links with the local authorities in the area and with the Scottish Special Housing Association became very close. The base would provide support facilities for the Third Submarine Squadron as well as the Tenth Submarine Squadron (as the POLARIS boats became) and this meant that workshop, stores and accommodation space had to be provided accordingly. A new jetty, with an extensive range of services (including, as a later modification, a heading check test facility for the submarine's navigation subsystem), had to be built: a range of workshops and test bays: emergency power sources: a separate Module Repair Facility for weapon system parts: a Calibration Laboratory: sleeping, eating, recreational and administrative accommodation: security installations: computer installations: playing fields, and so on – the variety of the components to the Base was, as the P L O reported to one Progress Meeting, "as nearly infinite as I can bear to contemplate".

(6) *House of Commons Debates*, Vol. 720, cols. 1332–3. The Prime Minister had been pressed on this matter since February 1965 by both sides of the House. See *House of Commons Debates*, Vol. 108, col. 1065, 16 March 1965; Vol. 709, cols. 1843–46; and Vol. 716, col. 1336. At a later period, other tests were carried out in order to maintain the effectiveness of the re-entry system design (see *The Guardian*, 22 October 1975 for a reference to a 1974 test and the possibility of another test in 1976, which was subsequently, and successfully, performed).

It was all rather slow to get under way. The PLO experienced the common 'chicken and egg' difficulties which have already been mentioned, but there were additional problems. The choice of Faslane imposed some of them particularly because local labour was more difficult for the contractors to come by and retain than had been expected. The attitude of contractors was not always as helpful as it could have been, although this was probably more due to the general state of the construction industry than to any particular reservations about the Faslane, or Coulport, contracts themselves. Relations with the Dumbartonshire County Council were generally good, and became good with the Helensburgh authorities, who were naturally concerned at the effects which a £47m development would have upon local affairs and amenities. In the run-up to the 1964 Election, the MPBW experienced some difficulty in obtaining Treasury authority to proceed with some contracts, and the SSHA was reluctant to commit its resources fully to a housing programme for which there was no local alternative use if the programme were to be cancelled by a new government; the result was that a great many items had not been put out to tender by October 1964,(7) and a great deal of effort had to be expended in the ensuing months towards creating a renewed sense of urgency in the programme for the Base.

There were four areas in which the plans for the Base did not work out as well as they might. The design underestimated service accommodation needs, although provision was made according to standard scales of expectation about the proportion of officers and men who would live in the Base or live with their families in the surrounding area; this led to some overcrowding of what had been intended to be above-par facilities.

Secondly, the importance of a fully developed industrial relations policy was rather under-played. There was an extensive dependence upon regular overtime, and a 'Clyde Base allowance' was allowed to grow up in a haphazard way, which created some difficulties when the Base became operational.

Thirdly, the managerial organisation of the Base proved to be unsatisfactory and had to be reshaped. The original scheme provided for over twenty senior managers to report directly to the Commodore, who quickly found the situation unbearable. Most of the department heads also had functional links to their parent organisations in the Navy Department, and it was not until an alternative scheme was devised and put into effect, embodying the devolution of much day-to-day responsibility, that the organisation settled down to work smoothly. The revised management structure has become a standard pattern for naval base organisations.(8)

The fourth problem area was the provision of automatic data processing equipment. In 1965, CPE had a run-in with the Ministry of Technology over their insistence on purchasing American-built machines for the ADP systems for the stores depots at Copenacre and Eaglescliffe, that

(7) Interview.
(8) Interview.

provided back-up spares for the submarines. Although it was Government policy to require departments to purchase British computer equipments and material wherever it was possible, no comparable British-built equipment was available in the required timescale, and those that could be made available were inadequate and, even the Treasury agreed, incompatible. The Minister of Technology, Mr. Frank Cousins, fought the issue but failed to persuade his colleagues.(9) Even though there were subsequent difficulties about mating the buildings for the computers with the hardware, CPE's proposals were undoubtedly cheaper and more efficient than the proposed alternatives could possibly have been.

But, partly because of this earlier *contretemps*, the selection of computer equipment for the Naval Stores stock control task at Faslane (which also covered pay-roll programmes) was approached with some caution. A committee, including Treasury representatives, was set up early in 1966 to review the preliminary choice of British equipments and programmes that had been made, on the basis of specifications and an element of competitive tendering. By November 1966, it became clear that some at least of the equipment would be delivered late, and thereafter the situation became increasingly unsatisfactory. Installation, and performance after installation, was beset by delays and breakdowns, and a Treasury investigation in the autumn of 1967 led to a decision to buy a standby equipment to provide a backup to a machine that seemed to be unable to have certain 'rogue' characteristics eliminated. As late as 1969, the Base staff, supported by ACP (as CPE had by then become) were complaining of the unreliability of the installed equipments and proposing measures to reduce the amount of stand-down time.

In the event, the Faslane Base, commissioned as HMS NEPTUNE, was not quite completed by the time of the first operational patrol, although all major services were functioning: the effluent disposal plant and some of the extra accommodation were not ready for use. Given the extent of the task that had been assumed, however, it was not a bad result; the essential services of the Base had been set to work sufficiently early for there to be no doubt about the ability to ensure RESOLUTION's material well-being.

(9) Interview.

CHAPTER NINE

Reflections

The processes by which technological innovation is organised appear, in practice, to display dynamic attributes which are not only inherent to the business of change which innovation represents but also require alterations in the boundaries of the divisions which have previously been established for the organisation of work; that is to say, innovation regularly alters both attitudes and institutions. One of the consequences of this phenomenon has been the emergence of designedly novel organisational structures that are intended to be more readily adaptive to innovatory circumstances, and better able to cope with the demands that they throw up. This pattern has been particularly noticeable where innovation has focussed on development and production tasks that require the combination of complex scientific, engineering and industrial components, which have frequently been organised, in traditional and hierarchically-fashioned units based upon staff functions, or technical specialisms, or phases of activity. The new demands, defined in effect by the desired innovation, have not matched either the boundaries or the established relationships between existing structures and have, as a consequence produced new, and specific, organisational patterns. These in turn are faced with problems that not only relate to the management of whatever the innovation may be but also to the new boundaries and the new relationships that now become the interface between the novel grouping and the old, or 'parent', structures.(1)

The notion of 'project management' that arises from these features is certainly not new; there are those who would claim that Noah was the first recorded 'project manager', and the title could certainly be attributed to Lloyd George for his work at the Ministry of Munitions in the First World War, as it was specifically attributed to General Leslie Groves, who managed the Manhattan Project in the Second World War. But the adoption, as a deliberate policy, of a distinctive method of management is relatively novel and has certain distinguishing characteristics. One is that project management is usually adopted as an organisational strategy against a background of compulsion; it may be a compulsion in

(1) Sapolsky identifies the policies that the Special Projects Office adopted in managing both innovation and the relationships to associated organisations: see Sapolsky, *op. cit.*, Ch. 2.

time or in money that arises from either a political or a commercial requirement to ensure success, but, underlying these positive objectives is an acceptance that they would be unlikely to be achieved by the existing organisations or procedures. So, particular attention has to be given to the other standard characteristics: new forms of administrative authority, financial discretion and management expertise; and in practice project management represents the eclipse of established technical disciplines and staff functions. Eclipse, but not necessarily supersession: because the project that is to be managed will, most commonly, represent only a partial transfer of function or responsibility. The organisational complex, in which project structures overlay existing administrative structures, and in which established functional and technical channels of responsibility co-exist with the new project responsibilities, has been termed "matrix organisation".(2)

Within a matrix complex, organisational structures may form and re-form, on the basis of projects whose boundaries will be set by the technical demands of the job in hand. Hence, "since the project organisation is essentially based upon the technological systems necessary to solve the problem represented by the project, it is structured according to the definitions of the various pieces of work that must be done".(3) As the task entrusted to the project organisation is accomplished, or changes, so the structure of the project organisation will adapt, to disappear or to re-form. In short, project organisations have been envisaged as specially designed tools for the accomplishment of specifically defined tasks: and an important part of the concept is that the objective is precisely delineated. Project management is therefore taken to represent an 'organic' organisational form, peculiarly capable of adapting to changing circumstances rather than a 'mechanical' structure likely to be outmoded by the course of events.(4)

But the element of compulsion or, to put it another way, the identification of a need to attribute priority to a specific task or objective, is also an instrumental factor in developing project organisations, that can be represented as a more general and perhaps even a more traditional feature of organisational development. The concern here is not with deciding which tasks *should* receive priority – that decision pre-dates the instrumental response – but with specifying the manner in which priority may best be identified and the structures or processes by which it can best be operationalised.

By 1960, and increasingly during the following decade, it was realised that priority could not effectively be attained for any particular program-

(2) See, for example, the work of D. R. Kingdon (*Matrix Organisation: Managing Information Technologies* (London, Tavistock, 1973)) and L. R. Sayles and M. K. Chandler (*Managing Large Systems: Organisation for the future* (New York, Harper and Row, 1971)).
(3) Kingdon, *op. cit.* page 60.
(4) The distinction between 'organic' and 'mechanical' forms was first made, and examined in some detail by T. Burns and G. Stalker in *The Management of Innovation* (London, Tavistock, 1961). It is elaborated in J. Woodward, *Industrial Organisation: Theory and Practice* (London, O.U.P., 1968) and P. R. Lawrence and J. W. Lorsch, *Organisation and Environment; Managing Differentiation and Integration* (Boston, Harvard 1967).

me – whether in government or industry – merely by designating a formal status or only by identifying the tasks which it had been decided should be dealt with more expeditiously within a general programme of work and a wider set of responsibilities. A label alone ensured nothing: it provided no substantative guarantee that the priority task would be able to compete more effectively with other tasks that also sought their share of limited resources and attention, and no range of sanctions, if the acquiescence towards the priority task that was implicit in the label was not conceded by other parts of the activity.(5) It became evident that, to achieve in any sort of real way the special status which the formal designation of priority was intended to accomplish, the chosen tasks would have to be set aside from the general context of standard organisations, procedures and responsibilities; and that to provide a greater measure of assurance that an accredited status of priority would facilitate the operation of a particular function over a prolonged period, a more demonstrative and specific structure had to be harnessed to the function.

Project styles of management and the establishment of project organisations provided the mechanism. In the later 1950s they were used in the British and United States government service selectively and sometimes in a rather tentative fashion but, as the 1960s passed, they were used more extensively, and with increasing enthusiasm, not merely to achieve priority but also to organise a range of weapon system programmes more coherently.(6)

The Polaris Executive was, therefore, an early example of the *genre*, and it stands as a good example of the success that can be achieved by such mechanisms. When it was set up it reflected primarily the requirement to endow a new task with a measure of real priority, and to give its managers a sufficient range of responsibilities to fulfil their goals. It was not therefore the type of project organisation, strictly speaking, that represented an organisational adaptation to the demands created by an emergent technology.(7) The technology, in substance, was already there; the amount of research and development was untypically low. But the transference of an unfamiliar technology imposed some, if not all, of the constraints associated with successful innovation and, arguably, the dependence upon a principal agent – in this case, Special Projects Office – introduced another untypical layer of relationships to be mastered. The definition of the duties and the scope of the Polaris Executive became, in

(5) Between 1951 and 1955 the government of the day accorded 'priority' and even 'super-priority' to a range of tasks in the defence and industrial fields caught up in the Korean war rearmament programme; but the results were extremely patchy.
(6) This development can be traced in the British government service, through the deliberations and reports of a number of investigation. See, for example: *Report of the Management Committee on the Management and Control of Research and Development* (London, HMSO, 1961) – otherwise known as the Gibb-Zuckerman report; the Ministry of Technology *Report of the Steering Group on Development Cost Estimating* (London, HMSO, 1969) – the Downey Report; the *Second Report from the Select Committee on Science and Technology, Defence Research HC213* (London, HMSO, 1969); and *Government Organisation for Defence Procurement and Civil Aerospace*, Cmmd 4641 (London, HMSO, 1971), which embodied the Rayner Report.
(7) A form discussed in Kingdom, *op. cit.*, see especially the foreword by Tvist.

a way that was not fully foreseen by Admiral Le Fanu, an outcome of the interaction between established organisational interests at three different levels: between the United Kingdom and United States governments: within the Admiralty: and between the Admiralty and other government departments, most crucially the Ministry of Aviation. And the definition also represented a compromise with the requirement for priority, that arose principally from the perceived need to protect other naval programmes from disproportionate effects. The net result, as it happened, was sufficient to the task, in the sense at least that it was made to work.

The operation of the Polaris Executive demonstrated that project organisation is not a means for consciously resolving the dilemmas associated with the setting of priorities. Attribution of a project's limits of authority should, ideally, follow after the decision to attribute priority, and may be rendered ineffective if a number of projects are set to compete against each other in similar or overlapping fields of activity. Project management reflects and enacts an ordering of priority; it is a device by which a choice once made can be adhered to, and an objective which has been identified as specially desirable can be pursued. It would be going too far to say that a multifunctional organisation such as a large government department can only successfully support one project organisation at a time; but it is equally clear that to hive off all new tasks, or large tasks, or salient tasks, within a department to a battery of projects is unlikely to be productive, and may easily become counterproductive, as the parent organisation is drained of resources and, probably, morale.

Given its status as a project, and given the absence of a dominant research and development function, the task environment of the Polaris Executive was primarily an institutional one – although it was nonetheless difficult and novel. Its operations were as much concerned with raising the performance standards and expectations of significant elements in the defence procurement process in the United Kingdom, and with fostering a consistently cooperative relationship with SP, as they were with the development of nuclear shipbuilding technology and its integration with the POLARIS weapon system. This role was reflected in the project management processes that were employed.(8)

Project organisation is ideally characterized by three basic features. First, the project itself must be sufficiently distinctive and discrete as a programme of work to require distinctive levels of competence and combinations of services over a period of time; thus, it is typically large and important, but not so demanding that it requires all the services of the parent organisation at the one time. Second, the management structure which the project is given has wider discretion, unusual limits of power and some freedom at least from prevailing procedures in the parent organisation. These exceptional limits of delegated authority must apply – though the degree of delegation may vary according to circumstances – to

(8) Institutional tasks are increasingly regarded as one of the central challenges that contemporary organisations have to meet. See, for example, Sir Geoffrey Vickers, *Making Institutions Work* (London; Associated Business Programmes, 1963) and H. A. Simon, *The Sciences of the Artificial* (Cambridge, Mass: M.I.T. Press, 1969).

the crucial functions of management, viz. budget, personnel and internal organisation. There is no optimal way to determine the best combination of discretion and authority in these areas, but discretion has to be sufficient in practice for the project organisation to claim, and for its environment consistently to accept, a distinctive competence and authority in its identified sphere of operations.(9)

The third feature of project organisation is that the life of the project is, ideally, a function of the objective that has been set. The project management may be granted exceptional powers, organisationally, to achieve the objective, conduct the associated tasks and resolve associated difficulties; but there is an implicit expectation that when all this has been accomplished, the project should disband, its functional utility having also passed away. The particular demands of new and different tasks will call for new project structures to be set up.

These attributes of project organisation are necessary, but not sufficient, conditions of project success. They have to be put to use by a management structure that is sufficiently self-aware to be willing to use them, and sufficiently capable to employ them to good effect. A successful project organisation is one that has deployed and employed its discretionary authority, distinctive competence and promotional licence to the limit afforded by its separate status: and done all this well. There is no guarantee, even as there was no guarantee in the mere declaration of priority, that a conglomeration of people and power will, of itself, ensure success. Success is self-generated by the exploitation of the opportunities that exceptional status presents, and by the de-fusing of institutional reactions that the grant of this status may create; the test is a record of substantive achievement, which has to be put alongside the exceptional status and may in the end displace it as the fundamental source of the project's real authority.

Nevertheless, exceptional status is crucial: and offers two sorts of opportunities. In the first place it creates a requirement to manage and to motivate the internal structures of the project organisation in distinctive ways. Wide discretion in the pursuit of a discrete objective can be used to generate a relatively well-defined sense of purpose and a specific innovatory impulse to improve upon – or short-circuit – established administrative processes. This is a cause as well as an effect, in the sense that the significance of the objective around which the project is formed is sufficiently urgent to transcend the utility of existing disciplines and organisations.

In the second place, these same factors can provide the project organisation with the capacity to manage its external environment successfully: to establish, and legitimise by achievement, the urgency of its task and elicit timely and appropriate responses. This is done, and arguably has to be done in order to be effective over time, without formal recourse to the sanctions implied in the stipulated authority that the project's

---

(9) The notion of 'distinctive competence' is examined by P. Selznick in *Leadership in Administration* (New York, Harper and Row, 1957).

remit provides to invoke compliance; the expectation must be sustained that the project organisation's unusual demands upon associated organisations are both appropriate and legitimate, and thus confer the obligation to provide a special response.

There was a direct comparability of style between the Polaris Executive and Special Projects Office in these matters of setting and structure. But, in detail, their relative status, the degrees of discretion they enjoyed, their range of responsibilities and their powers of decision were all quite different. Most notably, SP had much greater formal and informal authority; it also had a much wider task in its research and development function, and therefore, an inherently greater capacity to re-form, and technically to regenerate its task objectives. The general environment in which it operated was more benign and supportive; there was a well-espoused and unambiguous commitment to the continuous refinement of strategic nuclear weapon systems, and an increasing support for submarine-borne systems. In addition, SP fostered and employed a general political environment, based upon the Congress, to sustain a high level of support for the 'audit function'; it delivered the goods, in style and on time, and got political credit for doing so in a way that was not possible for the Polaris Executive to emulate. As a consequence, SP has been able to institutionalise itself, through a succession of technical advances, and in this way transcended the ideal-type of project organisation to become an institutionalised matrix organisation.(10)

By contrast, the Polaris Executive more nearly represents an ideal-type project in that its structure and functioning were radically changed on completion of its initial task. On the other hand, it could be argued that it did not have the full range of attributes, and power, that a completely standard project should, by definition, encompass. The budgetary and personnel authority was carefully qualified, and certainly never as wide as SP's, and the general environment was not as benign or supportive. Reservations within the Admiralty concerning the distinctiveness of the Polaris Executive at the outset specifically constrained the new organisation while the qualified commitment to strategic nuclear weapons, in the Navy no less than in the political arena, made the task, and by implication the lifespan, of the new structure contingent upon the performance of a time-constrained objective: to build and deploy a squadron of four submarines with the necessary support facilities.

Nevertheless, the performance of the Polaris Executive during this period was distinctive. The Nassau Agreement provided a radical change in circumstances for the Royal Navy's relationship to the national strategic deterrent force and for the Admiralty's procurement processes. It changed the limitations imposed by existing attitudes and established expectations; and the setting up of the Polaris Executive was a signal

(10) The study of how weapon system development gives rise to distinctive organisations and to successful bureaucratic politics has produced a number of interesting studies: e.g. T. Greenwood, *Making the MIRV* (Cambridge, Mass., Ballinger, 1975): R. E. Coulam, *Illusions of Choice* (Princeton, Princeton University Press, 1977): E. Beard, *Developing the ICBM* (New York, Columbia University Press, 1976) are three examples.

that the Admiralty was prepared to engage the challenge of these new circumstances. The operation of the Polaris Executive was a demonstration that in practice the Admiralty had the capacity and the innate talent to meet the challenge successfully.

CPE generated, and won acceptance for, a distinctive sense of competence and a novel sense of purpose which materially aided its progress. In the Special Projects Office it had an unusually cooperative partner and a distinctively successful pacesetter. It was able to exploit the initial conditions, which its creation acknowledged, and to turn them into substantive achievement.

But the work of CPE, and the effective span of life of the project organisation, cover only a part of the task which the Royal Navy assumed after the Nassau Conference. The maintenance and operation of the deployed deterrent force also call for careful organisation and the scrupulous fulfilment of defined responsibilities, involving many of the authorities which contributed to the Polaris Executive. Their roles may be somewhat different, and therefore the way in which their efforts are brought together are different; but the type of responsibility, to maintain a specialised activity having priority, is not all that different. It is, however, another story.

The Polaris Sales Agreement

Polaris Sales Agreement Between the Government of the United Kingdom of Great Britain and Northern Ireland and the Government of the United States of America

The Government of the United States of America and the Government of the United Kingdom of Great Britain and Northern Ireland, recalling and affirming the "Statement on Nuclear Defence Systems"(1) included in the joint communique issued on December 21, 1962, by the President of the United States of America and the Prime Minister of Her Majesty's Government in the United Kingdom of Great Britain and Northern Ireland, have agreed as follows:–

Article I

1. The Government of the United States shall provide and the Government of the United Kingdom shall purchase from the Government of the United States Polaris missiles (less warheads), equipment, and supporting services in accordance with the terms and conditions of this Agreement.
2. This Agreement shall be subject to the understandings concerning British submarines equipped with Polaris missiles (referred to in paragraphs 8 and 9 of the Nassau "Statement on Nuclear Defence Systems" agreed by the President of the United States and the Prime Minister at their meeting held in the Bahamas between December 18 and 21, 1962.

Article II

1. In recognition of the complexity of the effort provided for in this Agreement and the need for close coordination between the contracting Governments in giving effect to its terms, the two Governments shall promptly establish the organisational machinery provided for in the following paragraphs of this Article.

(1) Cmnd. 1915.

2. The Department of Defense, acting through the Department of the Navy, and the Admiralty or such other agency as the Government of the United Kingdom shall designate will be the Executive Agencies of their respective Governments in carrying out the terms of this Agreement. Appropriate representatives of the Executive Agencies are authorized to enter into such technical arrangements, consistent with this Agreement, as may be necessary.

3. A Project Officer will be designated by each Government's Executive Agency with direct responsibility and authority for the management of the activities of that Government under this Agreement. Each Project Officer will designate liaison representatives, in such numbers as may be agreed, who will be authorized to act on his behalf in capacities specified in technical arrangements and who will be attached to the Office of the other Project Officer.

4. A Joint Steering Task Group will be established by the Project Officers to advise them, *inter alia*, concerning the development of new or modified equipment to meet specific requirements of the Government of the United Kingdom, and concerning interfaces between the equipment provided by the two Governments respectively. The Joint Steering Task Group will comprise the Project Officers (or their representatives), and principal liaison representatives, and may include selected leaders from among the scientists, industrialists and government executives of the United Kingdom and of the United States. The Joint Steering Task Group will meet approximately every three months alternatively in the United Kingdom and in the United States under the chairmanship of the resident Project Officer.

Article III

1. The Government of the United States (acting through its Executive Agency) shall provide, pursuant to Article I of this Agreement, Polaris missiles (less warheads), equipment, and supporting services of such types and marks and in such quantities as the Government of the United Kingdom may from time to time require, and in configurations and in accordance with delivery programmes or time tables to be agreed between the Project Officers. In the first instance the missiles, equipment, and supporting services provided by the Government of the United States shall be sufficient to meet the requirements of a programme drawn up by the Government of the United Kingdom and communicated to the Government of the United States prior to the entry into force of this Agreement.

2. The missiles, equipment, and supporting services referred to in paragraph 1 of this article are the following:

    a. Polaris missiles (less warheads but including guidance capsules);
    b. missile launching and handling systems;
    c. missile fire control systems;
    d. ships navigation systems;

e. additional associated, support, test, and training equipment and services including, but not limited to:

   (i) test and check-out equipment, specialized power supplies, power distribution systems and support equipment associated with the items enumerated in subparagraphs a, b, c, and d. of this paragraph and adequate in type and quantity to meet the requirements of installations both aboard ship and ashore;

  (ii) specialized equipment including the types specified in subparagraphs a, b, c, d, and e.(i) of this paragraph for use in such support and training facilities as may be provided by the Government of the United Kingdom;

 (iii) construction spares and spare parts adequate in scope and quantity to ensure the continued maintenance of the equipment specified in subparagraphs a, b, c, d, e.(i), and e.(ii) of this paragraph;

 (iv) (a) latest available United States technical documentation including specifications, blueprints, and manuals covering the missiles and equipment listed in subparagraphs a, b, c, d, e.(i), e.(ii) and e.(iii) of this paragraph in sufficient scope and quantity to cover safety requirements and permit successful transport, installation, operation, and maintenance by the Government of the United Kingdom of all equipment purchased under the terms of this Agreement;

     (b) latest available United States technical documentation, as may be necessary from time to time in individual cases, to permit manufacture by the Government of the United Kingdom to the extent necessary for the maintenance, repair, and modification of the items listed in subparagraphs a, b, c, d, e.(i), e.(ii) and e.(iii) of this paragraph;

  (v) services including:

     (a) use, as appropriate, of existing support and missile range facilities in the United States;

     (b) assistance in programme management techniques and, in addition, those engineering and lead shipyard services required to ensure proper system integration, installation, and checkout in the United Kingdom; to the extent required and available appropriate modification, maintenance, and overhaul of the equipment listed in subparagraphs a, b, c, d, e.(i), e.(ii), e.(iii) of this paragraph;

     (c) research, design, development, production, test, or other engineering services as may be required to meet specific United Kingdom requirements;

     (d) training of naval and civil personnel in the service of the Government of the United Kingdom and United Kingdom contractors to the extent to which they are involved in the inspection, installation, operation, maintenance, repair, and modification of the equipment listed in subparagraphs, a, b, c, d, e.(i), e.(ii), e.(iii) of this paragraph.

Article IV

Future developments relating to the Polaris Weapon System, including all modifications made thereto, by the Government of the United States or the Government of the United Kingdom shall, in the areas enumerated in Article III, be made reciprocally available through their Executive Agencies in accordance with the terms of this Agreement, reciprocally applied.

Article V

The Government of the United Kingdom will provide the submarines in which will be installed the missiles and equipment to be provided under this Agreement, and will provide the warheads for these missiles. Close coordination between the Executive Agencies of the contracting Governments will be maintained in order to assure compatibility of equipment. Information concerning the hull, auxiliary machinery, and equipment of United States submarines transmitted under the authority of this Agreement will be such as is necessary to obtain a satisfactory interface between the equipment provided by the two Governments respectively. This Agreement does not, however, authorize the sale of, or transmittal of information concerning, the nuclear propulsion plants of United States submarines.

Article VI

1. In carrying out this Agreement, the Government of the United States will use, to the extent practicable, established Department of Defense contracting procedures and existing Polaris contracts. In any event contracts for production or work for the Government of the United Kingdom will be incorporated in or placed on the same terms as those for the Government of the United States. When appropriate the United States Project Officer will direct that amendments be sought to existing contracts and that terms be incorporated in new contracts to safeguard any special requirements of the Government of the United Kingdom in the contract subject matter which may arise in connection with this Agreement, for example, to provide for any alterations or any reduction of quantities which may be necessary.
2. The missiles and equipment provided by the Government of the United States under this Agreement shall be fabricated to the same documentation and quality standards as are the counterparts for the United States Polaris Program.
3. The missiles and equipment provided by the Government of the United States under this Agreement will be integrated with the scheduled United States Polaris Program and will be fabricated on a schedule which will make the most efficient and economical use of existing United States production lines. Deliveries will be made upon a schedule to be defined by

the Government of the United Kingdom, but which is consonant with the above fabrication schedule.

Article VII

1. The Government of the United States shall ensure that all supplies (which term throughout this Article includes, but without limitation, raw materials, components, intermediate assemblies and end items) which it will provide under this agreement are inspected to the same extent and in the same manner (including the granting of waivers and deviations) as are the counterparts for the United States Polaris Program. The United Kingdom Project Officer or his designated representative may observe the inspection process and offer his advice to the United States Government Inspector regarding the inspection, without delay to, or impairment of the finality of, the inspection by the Government of the United States.
2. The United States Project Officer through appropriate procedures will notify the United Kingdom Project Officer when final inspection of each end item will take place, and will furnish a certificate or certificates upon completion of each such inspection stating that this inspection has been made and that such end item has been accepted as having met all requirements of the relevant acceptance documentation (subject to any appropriate waivers and deviations). Copies of acceptance documentation and quality standards, together with reports required thereby, will be furnished to the United Kingdom Project Officer or his designated representative.
3. The Government of the United Kingdom will take delivery of the supplies as agreed pursuant to Article X following inspection, acceptance and certification by the Government of the United States. Delivery to the Government of the United Kingdom shall not relieve the Government of the United States from continuing responsibility for using its best endeavours thereafter to secure the correction or replacement of any items found not to have been manufactured in strict accordance with the documentation and quality standards referred to in Article VI or to be otherwise defective. Such corrections or replacements will be at the expense of the Government of the United Kingdom to the extent they are not covered by warranty or guarantee or otherwise recoverable by the Government of the United States.
4. The Government of the United States will use its best endeavours to obtain for or extend to the Government of the United Kingdom the benefit of any guarantees or warranties negotiated with United States contractors or subcontractors.

Article VIII

The Government of the United Kingdom shall indemnify and hold harmless the Government of the United States against any liability or loss resulting from unusually hazardous risks attributable to Polaris missiles or equipment identifiable, respectively, as missiles or equipment supplied or to be supplied to the Government of the United Kingdom under this Agreement. Unusually hazardous risks, for the purposes of this Agreement, are those defined by applicable statutes of the United States, or by any appropriate administrative act under the authority of such statutes, or held to exist by a court of competent jurisdiction. The Government of the United States shall give the Government of the United Kingdom immediate notice of any suit or action filed or of any claim made to which the provisions of this Article may be relevant. Representatives of the United Kingdom may be associated with the defence, before a court of competent jurisdiction, of any claim which may be borne in whole or in part by the Government of the United Kingdom. In procurement contracts for supplies and services made pursuant to this Agreement the Government of the United States is authorized to include unusually hazardous risk indemnification provisions substantially similar to those included in its own corresponding contracts.

Article IX

1. The Government of the United States will follow its normal procurement practices in securing all rights it considers to be essential to enable it to provide the missiles and equipment to be supplied to the Government of the United Kingdom under this Agreement. In addition, the Government of the United States shall notify the Government of the United Kingdom of any claim asserted hereafter for compensation for unlicensed use of patent rights alleged to be involved in the supply of such missiles and equipment to the Government of the United Kingdom, and the two Governments will consult as to the appropriate disposition of such claim.
2. The Government of the United Kingdom shall reimburse the Government of the United States for any payments made by the Government of the United States in settlement of liability, including cost and expenses, for unlicensed use of any patent rights in the manufacture or sale of the missiles and equipment supplied or to be supplied to the Government of the United Kingdom under this Agreement.

Article X

1. Delivery of equipment other than missiles to be provided under this Agreement for installation in submarines or supporting facilities to be provided by the Government of the United Kingdom shall be the responsibility of the Government of the United States and shall be made to those locations within the United Kingdom where the equipment is re-

quired. In addition to delivery of such equipment, the Government of the United States shall, subject to reimbursement for costs incurred, be responsible for providing such technical installation and testing services as are required by the Government of the United Kingdom for the satisfactory installation, check-out and testing of that equipment in submarines and supporting facilities of the United Kingdom.

2. Delivery of all missiles shall be made to appropriate carriers of the United Kingdom, or, if it is agreed, of the United States, at such United States supply points as are agreed by the Executive Agencies of both Governments. The Government of the United States shall be responsible for the initial check-out of all missiles provided under this Agreement.

Article XI

1. The charges to the Government of the United Kingdom for missiles, equipment, and services provided by the Government of the United States will be:
   a. The normal cost of missiles and equipment provided under the joint United States-United Kingdom production programme integrated in accordance with Article VI. This will be based on common contract prices together with charges for work done in United States Government establishments and appropriate allowance for use of capital facilities and for overhead costs.
   b. An addition of 5% to the common contract prices under subparagraph 1.a. of this Article for missiles and equipment provided to the United Kingdom, as a participation in the expenditures incurred by the Government of the United States after January 1, 1963, for research and development.
   c. Replacement cost of items provided from United States Government stock or, with respect to items not currently being procured, the most recent procurement cost.
   d. The actual cost of any research, design, development, production, test or other engineering effort, or other services required in the execution of this Agreement to meet specific United Kingdom requirements.
   e. The cost of packing, crating, handling and transportation.
   f. The actual costs of any other services, not specified above, which the Project Officers agree are properly attributable to this Agreement.

2. Payments by the Government of the United Kingdom in accordance with paragraph 1. of this Article shall be made in United States dollars. Payments to United States agencies and contractors shall be made, as they become due, from a trust fund which will be administered by the United States Project Officer. All payments out of the Trust Fund shall be certified to be in accordance with the terms of the Agreement. The Trust Fund will consist initially of a sum to be paid as soon as possible after entry into force of this Agreement and to be equivalent to the payments

estimated to fall due during the first calendar quarter of programme operations. Before the end of that quarter and of each succeeding quarter deposits shall be made by the Government of the United Kingdom with the object of having sufficient money in the Fund to meet all the calls which will be made upon it in the succeeding three months.

3. If at any time, the unexpended balance in the Trust Fund established pursuant to paragraph 2. of this Article falls short of the sums that will be needed in a particular quarter by the Government of the United States to cover:

    a. payment for the value of items to be furnished from the stocks of, or services to be rendered by, the Government of the United States;

    b. payment by the Government of the United States to its suppliers for items and services to be procured for the Government of the United Kingdom; and

    c. estimated liability or costs that may fall to be met by the Government of the United States as a result of termination of such procurement contracts at the behest of the Government of the United Kingdom;

the Government of the United Kingdom will pay at such time to the Government of the United States such additional sums as will be due. Should the total payments received from the Government of the United Kingdom prove to be in excess of the final total costs to the Government of the United States, appropriate refund will be made to the Government of the United Kingdom at the earliest opportunity with final adjustment being made within thirty days after determination of said final costs.

4. The United States Project Officer will maintain a record of expenditures under this Agreement in accordance with established Navy Special Projects Office Accounting procedures which record will be available for audit annually by representatives of the Government of the United Kingdom.

Article XII

1. The provisions of this Article concerning proprietary rights shall apply to the work referred to in subparagraph 1.d. of Article XI of this Agreement (hereinafter called in this Article "the work").

2. The Government of the United States shall ensure that the Government of the United Kingdom will receive a royalty-free, non-exclusive, irrevocable license for its governmental purposes:

    a. to practice or cause to be practiced throughout the world, all inventions conceived or first actually reduced to practice in the performance of the work; and

    b. to use or cause to be used throughout the world, all technical information first produced in the performance of the work.

3. In addition, the Government of the United States shall take the following steps to ensure the right of the Government of the United Kingdom to

reproduce, by manufacturers of its own choice, items developed in the performance of the work. In respect of those elements of this right not included in subparagraphs 2.a. and 2.b. of this Article, the Government of the United States shall:

  a. to the extent that it owns or controls such elements, accord free user rights to the Government of the United Kingdom;
  b. obtain the agreement of contractors and subcontractors performing the work to make available to the Government of the United Kingdom, on fair and reasonable terms and conditions, those elements which the contractor or sub-contractor owns or controls at the commencement of the work or acquires during the performance of the work;
  c. use its best endeavours to obtain for the Government of the United Kingdom or to assist the Government of the United Kingdom to obtain directly or through its own manufacturers, on fair and reasonable terms and conditions, elements of this right not covered by subparagraphs 2.a. and 2.b. of this Article.

4. The Government of the United States shall also ensure that the Government of the United Kingdom will receive the same rights as those referred to in paragraphs 2. and 3. of this Article in respect of any material now or hereafter covered by copyright produced or delivered in the performance of the work.

5. The Government of the United States shall furnish to the Government of the United Kingdom, in such quantities as may be agreed:

  a. all documentation obtained by the Government of the United States under contracts placed for the performance of the work;
  b. all documentation, owned or controlled by the Government of the United States, necessary for reproduction, by or on behalf of the Government of the United Kingdom, of items developed during the performance of the work.

6. It is understood that the Government of the United States will obtain for itself such of the rights referred to in subparagraphs 2.a., 2.b., and 3. of this Article as it may require for its governmental purposes.

7. The term "owned or controlled" as used in this Article means the right to grant a licence without incurring liability to any private owner of a proprietary or other legal interest.

8. The Government of the United States will use its best endeavours to ensure that there will be made available by United States manufacturers to the Government of the United Kingdom, on fair and reasonable terms and conditions, such technical assistance – for example, loan of engineers, or training – as the Government of the United Kingdom desires in order to permit the production by manufacturers of its own choice of the items developed in the performance of the work.

9. The Government of the United States will insert suitable provisions in all prime contracts for the work to ensure the availability to the Government of the United Kingdom of the rights, set forth in this Article, including a requirement that similar provisions be placed in subcontracts.

Article XIII

1. The Government of the United States, to the extent that it can do so without incurring liability to any private owner of a proprietary or other legal interest shall grant to the Government of the United Kingdom: (i) the right to reproduce and use, royalty-free, the technical documentation referred to in subparagraph 2.e.(iv) of Article III for the purposes stated in that subparagraph; and (ii) a non-exclusive, royalty-free licence to practice or cause to be practiced any invention for these purposes.
2. In respect of any part of the technical documentation referred in paragraph 1 of this Article which the Government of the United States cannot furnish to the Government of the United Kingdom without incurring a liability to a private owner of a proprietary or other legal interest, the Government of the United States will use its best endeavours to assist the Government of the United Kingdom in securing for the Government of the United Kingdom on fair and reasonable terms and conditions the right to use such documentation for the purposes stated in subparagraph 2.e.(iv) of Article III.

Article XIV

1. The Government of the United Kingdom shall not, without the prior express consent of the Government of the United States, transfer, or permit access to, or use of, the missiles, equipment, services, or documents or information relating thereto which are provided by the Government of the United States under this Agreement, except to a United Kingdom officer, employee, national or firm engaged in the implementation of this Agreement.
2. The Government of the United Kingdom shall undertake such security measures as are necessary to afford classified articles, services, documents or information substantially the same degree of protection afforded by the Government of the United States in order to prevent unauthorized disclosure or compromise.

Article XV

Annually, on or before the first of July, the Project Officers will prepare a formal joint report to the contracting Governments of action taken and progress made under this Agreement and a forecast of schedules and costs for completion. In addition, other more frequent joint reports will be submitted, as agreed upon by the Project Officers, to the heads of the Executive Agencies.

Article XVI

This Agreement shall enter into force on the date of signature.
IN WITNESS WHEREOF the undersigned, being duly authorized thereto by their respective Governments, have signed this Agreement.
DONE in duplicate at Washington this sixth day of April, 1963.

For the Government of the United States of America:
(Sd.) DEAN RUSK

For the Government of the United Kingdom of
Great Britain and Northern Ireland:
(Sd.) D. ORMSBY GORE

APPENDIX II

The Polaris Executive Organisation

Outline of the Polaris Executive Organisation 1963–67

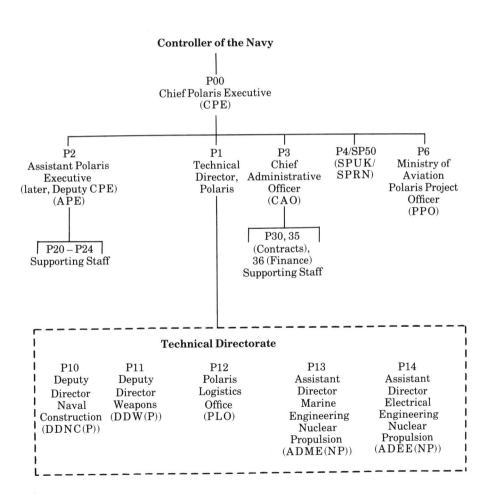

Controller of the Navy

P00
Chief Polaris Executive
(CPE)

P2
Assistant Polaris
Executive
(later, Deputy CPE)
(APE)

P1
Technical
Director,
Polaris

P3
Chief
Administrative
Officer
(CAO)

P4/SP50
(SPUK/
SPRN)

P6
Ministry of
Aviation
Polaris Project
Officer
(PPO)

P20 – P24
Supporting Staff

P30, 35
(Contracts),
36 (Finance)
Supporting Staff

Technical Directorate

P10
Deputy
Director
Naval
Construction
(DDNC(P))

P11
Deputy
Director
Weapons
(DDW(P))

P12
Polaris
Logistics
Office
(PLO)

P13
Assistant
Director
Marine
Engineering
Nuclear
Propulsion
(ADME(NP))

P14
Assistant
Director
Electrical
Engineering
Nuclear
Propulsion
(ADEE(NP))

APPENDIX III

The Management Staff

Polaris Executive Senior Management in the Construction and Deployment Period

Chief Polaris Executive
1963–1968   Rear-Admiral H. S. Mackenzie, DSO*, DSC*, later Vice-Admiral Sir Hugh Mackenzie, KCB, DSO*, DSC.*

1968–1971   (Assistant Controller, Polaris) Rear-Admiral Allan Trewby, later Vice-Admiral Sir Allan Trewby, KCB.

Technical Director
1963–1968   Rowland Baker Esq., OBE, Royal Corps of Naval Constructors, later Sir Rowland Baker, KCB, OBE.

1968–1971   Rear-Admiral C. W. H. Shepherd, CB, CBE.

Assistant (Later Deputy) Chief Polaris Executive
1963–1966   Captain J. R. McKaig, later Admiral Sir Rae McKaig, KCB, CBE.

1966–1968   Captain P. C. Higham, later Rear-Admiral P. C. Higham, CB.

Chief Administrative Officer
1963–1966   R. N. P. Lewin, Esq., CBE.

1966–1967   P. Nailor, Esq.

1967–1969   M. G. Power, Esq.

Polaris Project Officer, Ministry of Aviation
1963–1967   Rear-Admiral F. Dossor, CB, CBE.

1967–1969   S. A. Hunwicks, Esq.

Deputy Director of Naval Construction (Polaris)
1963–1967   S. J. Palmer, Esq., CB, OBE, Royal Corps of Naval Constructors.

1967–1969   H. J. Tabb, Esq., Royal Corps of Naval Constructors.

Deputy Director, Weapons (Polaris)

1963–1968   Captain C. W. H. Shepherd, later Rear-Admiral C. W. H. Shepherd, CB, CBE.

Polaris Logistics Officer

1963–1969   Captain L. Bomford

Assistant Director Marine Engineering (Nuclear Propulsion)

1963–1969   Captain L. D. Dymoke, later Rear-Admiral L. D. Dymoke, CB.

Assistant Director Electrical Engineering (Nuclear Propulsion)

1963–1968   H. C. Fitzer, Esq., CB, OBE.

Royal Navy Liaison Officer (Special Projects)

1963–1966   Captain P. G. La Niece, later Rear-Admiral P. G. La Niece, CB, CBE.
1966–1968   Captain C. H. Hammer, OBE.

Special Projects Liaison Officer

1963   Captain P. A. Rollings, USN.
1964–1966   Captain W. P. Murphy, USN.
1966–1968   Captain J. Love, USN.

APPENDIX IV

Programme Management Plans

Programme Management Plans were extensively used in the United Kingdom programme and in the Joint US–UK POLARIS programme, as a systematic method of identifying programme objectives and responsibilities. They consisted essentially of bar-charts, which described, in different levels of detail, the components and milestone activities in an area of work or task. The necessity of covering large areas of work concisely called for 'families' of PMPs; at the summary, or 'parent' level, a major component (e.g. 'machinery installation') might itself be embodied in a complete PMP breakdown at the secondary level. The following pages illustrate PMP construction, including the allocation of responsibilities for the achievement of the work described.

Chart 1

Specimen Programme Management Plan (SSBN04: Construction, Testin[g]
PROGRAMME MANAGEMENT PLAN – LONG TERM

Chart P10/4   December, 1967

Plan for.............................
SSBN 04
Construction, Testing and Commissioning.

MAJOR COMPONENTS
HULL CONSTRUCTION
HULL SERVICES AND OUTFIT
MACHINERY INSTALLATION
ELECTRICAL INSTALLATION
SONAR AND TORPEDO EQUIPMENT INSTALLATION
POLARIS SYSTEM INSTALLATION
TESTING

Responsibilities

Action Milestones

Direct	Suptng	Montng	Contr		Action Milestones
P15	DPT 10	CL	CL	1	▽ ○ Third Missile Unit to Berth
P15	DPT 10	CL	CL	2	▽ ○ Accomdn Unit No. 1 (Hull Unit 10) to Berth Position
P15	DPT 10	CL	CL	3	▽ ○ Accomdn Unit No. 2 (Hull Unit 11) to Berth Position
P15	DPT 10	CL	CL	4	☆ Complete Sonar Array on Jig
P15	DPT 10	CL	CL	5	▽ ○ Torpedo Compartment to Berth
P15	DPT 10	CL	CL	6	▽ ○ Fore End Construction to Berth
P13	DPT 6	CL	CL	7	▽ ○ Complete Shaft Bore
P13	DPT 3	CL	CL	8	○ Ship Reactor Pressure Vessel
P16	DPT 16	CL	CL	9	○ Complete Installation of Main Switchboard
P15	DPT 10	CL	CL	10	Complete Shielding ECT Closer
P13	DPT 18	CL	CL	11	○ Complete Final Checking of Sonar 2001 Array
P15	DPT 10	CL	CL	12	Complete Welding Primary Circuit
P15	DPT 10	CL	CL	13	Final Sight Torpedo Equipment
P10	DPT 10	CL	CL	14	Start Instal Launch Tubes
P16	DPT 16	CL	CL	15	Launch
P11	P111	CL	CL	16	Complete Pulling Main Cables
P15	DPT 10	CL	CL	17	Complete Phase 2 Fire Control Testing
P15	DPT 10	CL	CL	18	Complete MCC Air Balance
P13	DPT 18	CL	CL	19	Missile Hydraulics Complete
P15	DPT 10	CL	CL	20	Initial Fill
P13	DPT 3	CL	CL	21	Complete Installation of MASTS and PERISCOPES
P13	DPT 6	CL	CL	22	Load Core
P13	DPT 3	CL	CL	23	Main Turbines 1st Run
P10	DPT 10	Various	CL	24	Criticality
				25	CSTs

missioning)

1964	1965	1966	1967	1968	1969
JFM AMJ JAS OND	JFM AMJ JAS OND	JFM AMJ JAS OND	JFM AMJ JAS OND	JFM AMJ JAS OND	JFM AMJ JAS OND
JFM AMJ JAS OND	JFM AMJ JAS OND	JFM AMJ JAS OND	JFM AMJ JAS OND	JFM AMJ JAS OND	JFM AMJ JAS OND
1964	**1965**	**1966**	**1967**	**1968**	**1969**
			For'cst	R'sch'd	Ach'ved
Nov 66					2/67
Dec 66					2/67
Dec 66					2/67
Jan 67					11/66
Mar 67					30/5/67
Mar 67					16/6/67
May 67					7/67
Sep 67					28/9/67
Sep 67					
Dec 67					
Dec 67					
Feb 68					
Feb 68					
Mar 68					
Mar 68					
May 68					
Jun 68					
Jul 68					
Jul 68					
Aug 68					
Sep 68					
Nov 68					
Dec 68					
Mar 69					
May 69					
1964	**1965**	**1966**	**1967**	**1968**	**1969**

Chart 2

How the Programme Management Plan in constructed

The first part of the PMP is the **TITLE**. The TITLE contains a brief but accurate description of the TASK covered by the PMP:

Chart P10/4

```
┌─────────────────────────────────────┐
│                                      │
│   Plan for ........................  │
│                                      │
│                                      │
│             SSBN 04                  │
│                                      │
│                                      │
│        Construction, Testing         │
│        and Commissioning.            │
│                                      │
└─────────────────────────────────────┘
```

The next part of the PMP delineates the **MAJOR COMPONENTS** of the TASK described in the TITLE of the PMP:

PROGRAMME MANAGEMENT PLAN – LONG TERM

December, 1967

MAJOR COMPONENTS
HULL CONSTRUCTION
HULL SERVICES AND OUTFIT
MACHINERY INSTALLATION
ELECTRICAL INSTALLATION
SONAR AND TORPEDO EQUIPMENT INSTALLATIONS
POLARIS SYSTEM INSTALLATION
TESTING

MAJOR COMPONENTS represent general areas of work, or they may refer to particular sub-systems of the TASK. They are shown against time in such a way that they indicate a division into major types of work.

1964	1965	1966	1967	1968	1969
JFM AMJ JAS OND	JFM AMJ JAS OND	JFM AMJ JAS OND	JFM AMJ JAS OND	JFM AMJ JAS OND	JFM AMJ JAS OND
JFM AMJ JAS OND	JFM AMJ JAS OND	JFM AMJ JAS OND	JFM AMJ JAS OND	JFM AMJ JAS OND	JFM AMJ JAS OND

Thirdly, the PMP contains a list of MILESTONES. Each of these MILESTONES identifies some key event that must occur before the TASK outlined in the TITLE can be accomplished:

	ACTION MILESTONES
1	▽ ○ Third Missile Unit to Berth
2	▽ ○ Accomdn Unit No. 1 (Hull Unit 10) to Berth Position
3	▽ ○ Accomdn Unit No. 2 (Hull Unit 11) to Berth Position
4	☆ Complete Sonar Array on Jig
5	▽ ○ Torpedo Compartment to Berth
6	▽ ○ Fore End Construction to Berth
7	▽ ○ Complete Shaft Bore
8	○ Ship Reactor Pressure Vessel
9	○ Complete Installation of Main Switchboard
10	Complete Shielding ECT Closer
11	○ Complete Final Checking of Sonar 2001 Array
12	Complete Welding Primary Circuit
13	Final Sight Torpedo Equipment
14	Start Instal Launch Tubes
15	Launch
16	Complete Pulling Main Cables
17	Complete Phase 2 Fire Control Testing
18	Complete MCC Air Balance
19	Missile Hydraulics Complete
20	Initial Fill
21	Complete Installation of MASTS and PERISCOPES
22	Load Core
23	Main Turbines 1st Run
24	Criticality
25	CSTs

A MILESTONE usually identifies the beginning or the completion of a part of the TASK. In general, the completion of an activity has been found to be a more useful MILESTONE than the beginning of an activity in helping management control the accomplishment of the TASK. Other events vital to the programme may also constitute valid MILESTONES. The selection of MILESTONES is the most important activity in PMP preparation. This process of selection encourages programme planning which is both timely and comprehensive. MILESTONES wisely chosen can be of significant aid in programme control by helping 'management by exception'.

Next to each MILESTONE on the PMP is noted the planned DATE OF ACHIEVEMENT. MILES-TONES should be arranged in chronological order. To the right of the MILESTONE appears the TIME LINE, which enables quick reference to those MILESTONES that should be completed at any point in time. The last three columns should be headed up 'FORECAST', 'RESCHEDULED' and 'ACHIEVED' respectively. Revised dates should be entered in columns 1 or 2 when management decides that the original dates have become unrealistic. The ACHIEVED date column need only be completed when the actual date of achievement differs from the planned date. To the left of the MILESTONES spaces are left for MILESTONE STATUS SIGNALS. These signals, entered when appropriate, are shown to the right of the chart above.

	1964	1965	1966	1967	1968	1969
				For'cst	R'sch'd	Ach'ved
Nov 66						2/67
Dec 66						2/67
Dec 66						2/67
Jan 67						11/66
Mar 67						30/5/67
Mar 67						16/6/67
May 67						7/67
Sep 67						28/9/67
Sep 67						
Dec 67						
Dec 67						
Feb 68						
Feb 68						
Mar 68						
Mar 68						
May 68						
Jun 68						
Jul 68						
Jul 68						
Aug 68						
Sep 68						
Nov 68						
Dec 68						
Mar 69						
May 69						
	1964	1965	1966	1967	1968	1969

☆ (blue) MILESTONES achieved ahead of schedule.

○ (green) MILESTONES achieved on schedule.

□ (orange) MILESTONES not expected to be achieved on schedule.

▽ (red) MILESTONES missed.

○ ▽ MILESTONES achieved late.

Chart 3

The types of responsibility described

Finally, each PMP contains a list of RESPONSIBILITIES, four for each MILESTONE:

Responsibilities

Direct	Suptng	Montng	Contr
P15	DPT 10	CL	CL
P15	DPT 10	CL	CL
P15	DPT 10	CL	CL
P15	DPT 10	CL	CL
P15	DPT 10	CL	CL
P15	DPT 10	CL	CL
P13	DPT 6	CL	CL
P13	DPT 3	CL	CL
P16	DPT 16	CL	CL
P15	DPT 10	CL	CL
P15	DPT 10	CL	CL
P13	DPT 18	CL	CL
P15	DPT 10	CL	CL
P15	DPT 10	CL	CL
P10	DPT 10	CL	CL
P16	DPT 16	CL	CL
P11	P111	CL	CL
P15	DPT 10	CL	CL
P15	DPT 10	CL	CL
P13	DPT 18	CL	CL
P15	DPT 10	CL	CL
P13	DPT 3	CL	CL
P13	DPT 6	CL	CL
P13	DPT 3	CL	CL
P10	DPT 10	Various	CL

Classification RESTRICTED

These RESPONSIBILITIES are defined as follows:–

DIRECT — The person within the Polaris Executive charged with the job of seeing that the MILESTONE is achieved. *Note:* In some cases it might be necessary to show here a section rather than an individual.

SUPPORTING — The person or organisation within or outside the Polaris Executive whose assistance is essential for the accomplishment of the MILESTONE.

MONITORING — The person or organisation within or outside the Polaris Executive who cannot get on with his own tasks until the MILESTONE is achieved.

CONTRACTOR — The organisation which performs the actual work necessary to achieve the MILESTONE.

These four RESPONSIBILITIES for each MILESTONE enable management at any level to pinpoint responsibility for any phase of the TASK described in the TITLE.

The symbol VAR should not be used in the RESPONSIBILITIES columns. All the responsible authorities or individuals should be listed, either on the form or on a separate sheet of paper. Where possible a co-ordinating authority should be agreed and identified by the PMP sponsor when "multiple responsibilities" are likely to occur.

In joint US/UK PMP's milestone responsibility will normally be designated as 'AC(P)', 'SPRN', 'SP Branch' or 'US Contractor' only, the appropriate staff officer within each authority being a matter of internal organisation. But where the PMP sponsor is able to pinpoint responsibility within these authorities with accuracy, he should do so.

APPENDIX V

Bibliography

This Bibliography is selective, in the sense that it concentrates upon publications that have been referred to, or are directly relevant to, the text; but it is also intended to offer a guide to further reading.

Official publications

Cmnd. 537	Agreement for Cooperation on the Uses of Atomic Energy for Mutual Defence Purposes.
Cmnd. 859	Amendment to Agreement for Cooperation on the Uses of Atomic Energy for Mutual Defence Purposes, of July 3, 1958.
Cmnd. 1915	Joint Communique and Statement on Nuclear Defence Systems, December 1962.
Cmnd. 1995	Polaris Sales Agreement April, 1963.
Cmnd. 2937	Shipbuilding Inquiry Committee, 1965–1966, Report.
H.C. 213	Second Report from the Select Committee on Science and Technology. Defence Research of the Steering Group on Development Cost Estimating; London: HMSO, 1969.
Cmnd. 4641	Government Organization for Defence Procurement and Civil Aerospace; 1971.
H.C. 399	Expenditure Committee: Twelfth Report, 1972–3 *Nuclear Weapons Programme*. 19 July 1973.

Books and Theses

BARTLETT, C. J. *The Long Retreat*; London, Macmillan, 1972.
BAYLIS, J. *Anglo-American Defence Relations 1939–80: The Special Relationship*; London, Macmillan, 1981.
BEARD, E. *Developing the ICBM*; New York, Columbia U.P., 1976.

BUCHAN, A. F. *NATO in the 1960s*; London, Chatto and Windus (revised edition) 1963.

BURNS, T. and STALKER, G. *The Management of Innovation*; London, Tavistock, 1961.

COULAM, R. E. *Illusions of Choice*; Princeton, Princeton U.P., 1977.

CROWE, W. J. *The Policy Roots of the Modern Royal Navy, 1946–63* (Ph.D., Dissertation, Princeton University, 1965).

DILLON G. M. *Dependence and Deterrence*, Aldershot, Gower, 1983.

DRIVER, C. *The Disarmers, a study in protest*; London, Hodder and Stoughton, 1964.

ENTHOVEN, A. C. and SMITH, K. W. *How Much Is Enough?*; New York, Harper and Row, 1971.

FREEDMAN, L. W. *Britain and Nuclear Weapons*; London, Macmillan, 1980.

GOWING, M. *Britain and Atomic Energy, 1939–45*; London, Macmillan, 1964.

GOWING, M. *Independence and Deterrence*; London, Macmillan, 1974 (2 volumes).

GREENWOOD, T. *Making the MIRV*, Cambridge, Mass, Ballinger, 1975.

GROOM, A. J. R. *British Thinking About Nuclear Weapons*; London, Frances Pinter, 1974.

HEWLETT, R. G. and DUNCAN, F. *Nuclear Navy, 1945–62*; London, University of Chicago Press, 1974.

HUNTER, R. E. *Politics and Polaris: The Special Projects Office of the Navy as a Political Phenomenon*; Wesleyan University, June, 1962 (B.A. Thesis).

KINGDON, D. R. *Matrix Organisation: Managing Information Technologies*; London, Tavistock, 1973.

LAWRENCE, P. R. and LORSCH, J. W. *Organisation and Environment: Managing Differentiation and Integration*; Boston, Harvard University Division of Research Graduate School of British Administration, 1967.

MACMILLAN, H. *At the End of the Day*; London, Macmillan, 1973.

McGEOCH, I. *The British POLARIS Project*; Edinburgh University, 1975 (M.Phil. thesis).

MENDL, W. *Deterrence and Persuasion, French Nuclear Armament in the Context of National Policy, 1945–69*; London, Faber and Faber, 1970.

NEUSTADT, R. E. *Alliance Politics*; New York, Columbia U.P., 1970.

PIERRE, A. J. *Nuclear Politics*; London, O.U.P., 1972.

ROSECRANCE, R. N. *Defense of the Realm*; London, Columbia U.P., 1968.

SANDERS, D. *The Politics of Defense Analysis*; New York, Dunellan, 1973.

SAPOLSKY, H. M. *The Polaris System Development*; Cambridge, Mass., Harvard U.P., 1972.

SAYLES, L. R. and CHANDLER, M. K. *Managing Large Systems: Organisations for the future*; New York, Harper & Row, 1971.

SELZNICK, P. *Leadership in Administration*; New York, Harper and Row, 1957.

SIMON, H. A. *The Sciences of the Artificial*; Cambridge, Mass., M.I.T. Press, 1969.

SPIERS, M. *Techniques and Public Administration*; London, Fontana, 1973.

STEINBRUNER, J. D. *The Cybernetic Theory of Decision*, Princeton, Princeton U.P., 1974.

VICKERS, Sir Geoffrey *Making Institutions Work*; London, Associated Business Programmes, 1973.

WILSON, H. *Labour Government, 1964–70; A Personal Record*; London, Michael Joseph and Weidenfeld and Nicolson, 1971.

WOODWARD, J. *Industrial Organization: Theory and Practice*; London, Oxford U.P., 1968.

ZUCKERMAN, S. *Nuclear Illusion and Reality*; London, Collins, 1982.

Reports and Pamphlets

BEATON, L. The Western Alliance and the McNamara Doctrine (Adelphi Paper No. 11); London, Institute for Strategic Studies, 1964.

BOW GROUP, Conservative Party. Stability and Survival, a Bow Group Discussion about Defence Policy; London, Bow Group, 1961.

BUCHAN, A. F. The Multilateral Force, an historical perspective (Adelphi Paper No. 13); London, Institute for Strategic Studies, 1964.

DE WEERD, H. A. The Labour Party and Unilateralism; RAND Memorandum, RM2914-PR, 1962.

ECONOMIST "Polaris Submarines: a surprising amount of fall-out"; 20 April 1968.

HUGHES, E. Polaris and The Arms Race; London, Fabian Society, 1965.

KEMP, G. Nuclear Forces for Medium Powers (Adelphi Papers 106–107); London, International Institute for Strategic Studies, 1974.

MARTIN, L. W. British Defence Policy: The Long Recessional (Adelphi Paper No. 61); London, Institute for Strategic Studies, 1969.

NUCLEAR ENERGY. The Polaris Submarine Programme; November–December 1967.

SHIPBUILDING AND SHIPPING RECORD. "RESOLUTION: first Polaris missile submarine for the Royal Navy"; 19 September 1967.

SMART, I. Future Conditional: the Prospect for Anglo French Nuclear Cooperation (Adelphi Paper No. 78); London, Institute for Strategic Studies, 1971.

WELDING AND METAL FABRICATION. "Modernisation at Cammell Laird", July 1963.

Articles and Periodicals

ARMSTRONG, W. E. I. and FEAZEY, M. J. Shipyard reconstructed for Polaris Submarines: *The Dock and Harbour Authority* (Vol. XLVIII) No. 569, March 1958.

BEATON, L. Facts about Skybolt: *New Scientist* (No. 275), 22 February 1962, pp. 430–1.

BRANDON, H. SKYBOLT, the full inside story of how a missile nearly split the West: *The Sunday Times*, 8 December 1963.

BROWN, N. Britain's Strategic Weapons: (1) Manned Bombers, (2) The Polaris A3: *The World Today*, Vol. XX, July–August 1964, pp. 293–8, 358–64.

BUCHAN, A. F. Nassau Reconsidered: *New Republic*, 2 March 1963.

FELD, T. F. Britain's deterrent and the Decision to Abandon the Blue Streak Missile: *NATO's Fifteen Nations*, February–March 1962, pp. 27–31.

GORDON WALKER, P. C. The Labour Party's Defence and Foreign Policy: *Foreign Affairs*, Vol. XLII(3), April 1964, pp. 391–8.

HUNTER, E. H. Quality Control for a POLARIS Submarine: *Welding and Metal Fabrication* (Vol. 35), November 1967.

MARTIN, L. W. The Market for Strategic Ideas in Britain: The Sandys Era: *American Political Science Review*, Vol. LV(i), 1962, pp. 23–41.

NEUSTADT, R. E. Memorandum on the British Labour Party and the MLF: *New York Review of Books*, Vol. XI(10), 5 December 1958, pp. 37–46.

SHEPHERD, Captain C. W. H. "The United Kingdom Polaris Project": *Journal of the Royal Aeronautical Society*, (Vol. 70), September 1966.

SIMPSON, J. "The Polaris Executive". A Case Study of a Unified Hierarchy, *Public Administration*, Vol. 48, Winter 1978.

SIMPSON, J. Lessons of the British Polaris Project: An Organisational History. *Journal of the Royal United Services Institution*, March 1969, pp. 46–50.

TABB, H. J. and WARREN, S. A. T. Quality Control Applied to Nuclear Submarine Construction: *Royal Institute of Naval Architects Quarterly Transactions*, Vol. 108, July 1966.

TABB, H. J. and WARREN, S. A. T. Quality Control Applied to Nuclear Submarine Construction: *Shipping World and Shipbuilder*, 16 July 1967.

WEALLANS, J. W. and ALLEN, B. Towards Automating the TIG Welding Process: *Welding and Metal Fabrication*, (Vol. 37), March 1969.

WHITESTONE, N. E. Progress with Polaris: *Brassey's Annual*, London, 1966 (pp. 129–134).

Printed in the United Kingdom for Her Majesty's Stationery Office
Dd 289713   C20   5/88   0443/5   8206